Frontiers

03

Frontiers

03

New writing on
cutting-edge science
by leading scientists

Edited by Tim Radford
Foreword by Richard Fortey

Atlantic Books
London

First published in 2003 by Atlantic Books,
on behalf of Guardian Newspapers Ltd.
Atlantic Books is an imprint of Grove Atlantic Ltd.

10 9 8 7 6 5 4 3 2 1

A CIP catalogue record for this book is available from the British Library

ISBN 1 84354 017 7

Printed in Great Britain by The Cromwell Press, Trowbridge

Design by Bryony Newhouse

Grove Atlantic Ltd
Ormond House
26–27 Boswell Street
London WC1N 3JZ

CONTENTS

ix   *Preface*   TIM RADFORD

xii   *Foreword*   RICHARD FORTEY

1   Staring at faces from the past
HENRY GEE Sahelanthropus tchadensis, *better known as Toumaï, is the man of the year, and the find of the century.*

11   Scramjets: the wind beneath their wings
JONATHAN GLANCEY *After one hundred years of flight, air travel is due a revolution.*

20   Biodiversity and the case of the missing lynx
MARK COLLINS AND ADRIAN NEWTON *Wilderness areas are being destroyed so why do we think it doesn't affect us?*

28   Stem cells: life is what you make of it
ARLENE JUDITH KLOTZKO *New medical technologies involving embryo tissue seem only to raise major new moral questions.*

35   Dinosaurs: see how they run
TIM RADFORD *They could take the heat, they could stand the cold, but could they sprint?*

39   Punning machines
PETER FORBES *Nature's engineers got there before us.*

49 Global warming: where are the snows of yesteryear?
TIM RADFORD *The snows of Kilimanjaro are disappearing fast. But that's not all.*

53 Cloning: a show called Cats
TIM RADFORD *Cc owes her life to a millionaire's pet project.*

56 Supersymmetry: too beautiful to be wrong?
GRAHAM FARMELO *String, squarks, sparticles and the answer to everything (maybe).*

63 The Johannesburg summit and down to earth in Alex
BEN WISNER *How world agreements could help the poor or fill the pockets of the rich.*

71 Malaria: the secrets of a killer
NEIL HALL *The unravelling of the genetic machinery of malaria and the mosquito that carries it.*

75 Genome sequencing: Wellcome news?
JANE ROGERS *How much more can we learn about ourselves from mouse DNA?*

82 Mathematicians and the war on terror
KEITH DEVLIN *In 2002, statisticians suddenly found themselves in the front line in the battle against terrorism.*

88 Why genomics could be a disaster for medical science
DAVID HORROBIN *Do fifty years of DNA add up to a golden year for the geneticists?*

95 Depression: we think as we feel
LEWIS WOLPERT *The brain may be more a creature of its moods than anyone expected.*

100 How the brain handles numbers
BRIAN BUTTERWORTH *Birds do it, apes do it, even uneducated frogs do it but some children just cannot count.*

108 Quantum computers and the quest for the Dream Machine
PAUL DAVIES *A quantum computer could, in theory, out-compute the whole universe and become the ultimate virtual reality machine.*

116 **Lab rats: the remote-controlled rodent roadshow**

TIM RADFORD *Meet roborat, mobile at the click of a mouse and ready to go anywhere.*

118 **How little we know about the uncertainty principle**

PHILIP BALL *Heisenberg's uncertainty principle has made the quantum leap from the lab to popular language. But it doesn't mean quite what everyone thinks it means.*

122 **Life in the cosmos... and under our feet**

DUNCAN STEEL *Scientists are using a surprising variety of approaches in their quest for clues as to whether we are indeed 'alone'.*

131 **Non-lethal weapons: lasers, phasers, Tasers, Dazers and People Zappers**

DAVID HAMBLING *The latest developments in directed energy weapons.*

136 **Animal behaviour: what's in a mane?**

TIM RADFORD *Why brunettes are hot stuff.*

138 **Crows and tools**

TIM RADFORD *What a bird brain can really achieve.*

141 *Notes on contributors*

Preface

TIM RADFORD

Fifty years ago, in 1953, in Cambridge, the British Francis Crick and the American James Watson, building on evidence from Maurice Wilkins and Rosalind Franklin at King's College, London, deciphered the structure of DNA. This is the molecule that carries the code for all life, and replicates it. In 1962, Crick, Watson and Wilkins shared the Nobel prize. By then Rosalind Franklin was dead. It was the start of a dizzying revolution marked in 2002 by the completed DNA printouts of rice, the laboratory mouse, the malarial mosquito and the malaria parasite, the pufferfish and a host of other organisms, and it was the foundation for a new kind of biology, sealed by yet more Nobel prizes for British and American scientists in 2001 and 2002.

But it was not the only revolution. In 1953, the idea of space travel was little more than fantasy. In 2003 – just 100 years after the first heavier-than-air flight – a British lander will touch down on the surface of Mars and a European spacecraft will set off for a rendezvous with a comet. In 1953, cosmology was not regarded as a serious science. Today, any conjecture about the history of the universe is limited to events within the first thousandth of a second of time, 15 billion years ago. In 1953, the world's few computers were huge, cripplingly expensive and of limited potential. Now a laboratory in the north-west has just installed a parallel processor that could do a year's mathematics homework for every child in Britain in one fifth of a second and seven-year-olds play with computers that routinely outperform those NASA used to get Apollo astronauts to the moon.

In 1953, the planet itself was a puzzle. Why were there sea shells high in the Himalayas? Why were there volcanoes in Iceland and earthquakes deep under the Andes? Why did the coast of Brazil seem to fit so tantalizingly into the coast of West Africa? Today the Earth is understood to be a dynamic system, and the continents as continually moving fragments, bumping together and tearing apart over billions of years as they ride on the conveyor belt of the ocean floor, itself being newly created and destroyed as volcanoes and earthquakes occur at tectonic plate boundaries. In 1953, the term 'brain research' seemed a contradiction. How could humans understand the very thing they used do any understanding? Neuroscience is now a huge new frontier and researchers have begun to map the machinery of mind itself. In 1953, robots figured in science fiction only. In 2002, the industrial robot population of the world passed the one million mark and researchers planted electrodes in the brain of a live, sentient rat and turned it into a remotely-controlled agent that could be made to run to wherever they chose. All this has happened within the working lifetime of Crick, Watson and Wilkins. At the time of writing this preface, in the dying days of 2002, all three were still in some degree active in science and taking an interest in the extraordinary scientific events of the year.

It was the year in which scientists traced the ancestry of Bulldog, Basset Hound and St Bernard to a handful of wolves in China 15,000 years ago, and worked out how a gecko could run up a vertical polished glass wall. Geologists studied tiny spherules of glass in the west of England and linked them to shrapnel from an asteroid strike in Canada 214 million years ago. An Australian mathematician identified the best way to lace a shoe (and found that centuries of trial and error had already achieved the optimal result). Scientists in Manchester calculated how ancient Greek athletes used weights on their wrists to gain extra inches in the long jump. Australian researchers announced that they had 'teleported' information between laser beams a metre apart. American defence researchers fitted tiny radio-transmitter backpacks to honey bees and trained them to sniff for dangerous explosives. A team in Baltimore, Maryland, combined the light from 200,000 galaxies and pronounced the merged colour of the universe to be pale turquoise. A few weeks later they announced, red-faced, that they had made a mistake: the real colour was a disappointing beige. Forensic teams reconstructed the last meals of Otzi the Iceman, the bronze age hunter who was found frozen and mummified by an Alpine glacier in 1991 (he dined off ibex and then venison). And a psychologist in Hertfordshire ended a year of research, involving submissions from 2 million people in 70 nations, and identified the world's funniest joke. By the end of the year, humour had ceased to be rib-tickling. 'If I hear one more joke I'm going to punch someone,' he said.

Most of these stories did not make it into *Frontiers 03*. This is the second book in a series that tries to trace the scientific landmarks of a year just ended, and to go a little deeper into a few of the contemporary themes of science and technology. Without the support and encouragement of Toby Mundy and Alice Hunt at Atlantic Books, it could not have been completed. Without the support and encouragement of Alan Rusbridger, editor of the *Guardian*, it could not have even begun. And without the generous contributions of the working scientists and seasoned writers in the pages that follow, there would, of course, be no *Frontiers 03* at all.

December 2002

Introduction

RICHARD FORTEY

At the western end of the Natural History Museum in London there
is a pristine, gleaming glass palace – the Darwin Centre, a spare, twenty-
first century addition to Waterhouse's wonderful, ornament-encrusted
Victorian extravaganza. Its opening on 30 September 2002 marked a new
phase in the history of scientific collections. Museums have always had
a tradition of locking biological materials away from the public gaze, a
culture of safeguarding them in secret for posterity. In the Darwin Centre,
there are 22 million zoological specimens preserved in jars of 'spirit' –
alcohol, of course – but in the case of nineteenth-century specimens this
might even have included ship's rum. Fish, reptiles and crustaceans from
anywhere in the world are arrayed in glass jars, labelled with their locality
and collector. Many of them are type specimens – collections of species
whose identity and scientific name are established in perpetuity. It is
a kind of reference library for global biodiversity, a roll-call of the
living world.

In the basement there are huge glass jars holding depressed-looking
sharks, Komodo dragons and other exotica which make Damien Hirst's
preparations look like a rehearsal for the real thing. This is where research
on the identity of animals is carried out by a team of dedicated specialists,
nowadays supplemented by the most cutting-edge molecular techniques
but still, ultimately, rooted in the ground truth of preserved collections.
Until the Centre opened, this was an hermetic world in which experts
laboured away unseen, producing monographs for others of their
coterie. Not any more. Now the public can wander in among the glass

jars. Scientists from behind the scenes are on hand to explain the work they do, and why it matters.

The massive changes humankind is wreaking on the world have given a genuine urgency to the preservation of permanent records of the planet's biological richness. Sometimes – and how sad it is – a pickled museum specimen may be all that remains of a vanished species, the only enduring record of our rapacity and foolishness. These specimens have a poignancy and uniqueness which no *objet d'art* in a more conventional museum can match. Usually, however, specimens relate to ongoing research concerning problems as diverse as deep-sea fish, parasite vectors or the evolutionary explosion of crustaceans which has taken place in the Caspian Sea. We still have so much to discover about the diversity of the biological world, and the general public who visit the Darwin Centre should be able to feel that they, too, are part of the process of discovery and that they share the responsibility for maintaining ecosystems that have taken more than 3000 million years to establish. Science, in the case of the Darwin Centre, has almost literally come out of the closet.

I believe that the Darwin Centre is an appropriate symbol for what scientists have to do in 2003 – and in the future. There has never been a wider interest in science among the lay public – nor, apparently, a more general distrust. Scientists, at least for some, have become part of the nebulous 'they', such as in 'Next thing you know, they will be producing genius clones in test tubes.' The fact is that most scientists do not work on anything to do with cloning, GM foods or weapons of mass destruction or, indeed, anything which 'they' might be plotting. This majority of scientists might with some justice feel aggrieved at being lumbered with the Dr Strangelove image. Most scientists are open about what they do and are delighted when a wider audience takes an interest. If scientists as a whole have a failing, it is that they tend to be so immersed in their work that they would like to be left alone just to get on with it. Perhaps they feel most comfortable inside that closet. In this reclusiveness, they are probably no different from many other creative people. It's just that people do not need to question what it is that a novelist actually does. But if the public is not to demonize science, it is ever more necessary to expose its workings to scrutiny, even if it means taking time out from the test tubes.

Science journalists have a valuable role in what the French call *haute vulgarisation*. Most are on the side of scientists: were they not, they would find it difficult to get a story. Many pose useful and legitimate questions about the nature of research, including genomics and GM crops. A precious few have a talent for rendering understandable the more arcane areas of mathematics. Along with a minority of academics with a talent for wider communication, science writers play a vital part in building bridges between the laboratory and the man on the Clapham omnibus. A fine collection of articles exemplifying the art is gathered together in this book. Not all the essays espouse the cause of scientist as hero, and that is exactly as it should be. Science prospers best in a democratic ethos and the dissenting voice is an essential part of democracy.

Charles Darwin summarized his research in books that sold directly to the readers. Modern science reaches its audience by a less direct route: publication in a science journal couched in the esoteric language of the speciality always comes first. Communicating with a wider public requires a subsequent shift in language. In a peculiar way, jargonized scientific language is another secret closet. To escape from it requires a kind of exposure, in the same way as those hidden fishes have been extricated from the bowels of the Natural History Museum. Science requires intelligent scrutiny by those who ultimately pay for it and by those who will benefit from it in the long run. Nor should the benefits be reckoned in new cures or gadgets alone. A sense of wonder at the workings of nature should be the common goal of scientist and writer alike.

Oxford, December 2002

Frontiers

03

Staring at faces from the past

HENRY GEE

Sahelanthropus tchadensis, better known as Toumaï, is the man
of the year, and the find of the century.

When I joined the scientific journal *Nature* as a junior reporter in
1987, the then editor John (now Sir John) Maddox told me two things.
The first was about politics. 'In this job', he said, 'you will make enemies'.
I have since derived a curious solace from these words – especially after
I moved to the editorial desk, to be harangued by the outraged scientists
whose research papers I had summarily rejected.

The second was about hype. I soon learned that *Nature* had many
banned words. One of them was 'major'; another was 'breakthrough'.
To use one or other was unfortunate – to use them in conjunction was
simply careless. The reason was clear, said Maddox. Most scientific
advances are incremental, like small bricks added to a wall that is already
huge. Major Breakthroughs occur when two bricks happen to be added

I

at once. I took these words to heart and have never, to my knowledge, used the words 'major breakthrough' to describe a scientific advance.

This wisdom came to haunt me one sunny morning in the late autumn of 2001, while standing on the Paris-bound platform of Poitiers railway station, in central France. For I had just learned of something that could honestly be hailed as a Major Breakthrough. And more than that, I had held it in my two hands.

I am talking of the remarkably well-preserved skull of an extinct hominid – that is, a member of the human family of species – discovered in the remote and inhospitable Djurab desert of northern Chad in central Africa, by Djimdoumalbaye Ahounta, a member of a multi-national team lead by veteran fossil-hunter Michel Brunet of the University of Poitiers. The creature was eventually to acquire a formal, zoological name, *Sahelanthropus tchadensis*. For now, it had a nickname, 'Toumaï'. Shorter and more evocative than the formality required by zoology, Toumaï is a name given to a child born just before the dry season in that parched region. It means 'Hope of Life'.

Steve Bell, 12 July 2002.

Toumaï is believed to represent the earliest representative of our lineage, after it became distinct from the pedigree that leads to modern chimpanzees and gorillas. This is not, however, the same as saying that it was 'our ancestor'. The best we can do is say that it was more closely related to us than to any animal now alive. But the big shocker was its antiquity. Toumaï is between six and seven million years old, and probably closer to seven than six.

Given the heaving masses of humanity found on Earth today, it may be a surprise to learn that hominids were never common until relatively recently, after the invention of agriculture about ten thousand years ago prompted a population explosion that continues today. A dozen or so species of hominid are recorded from the fossil record (the precise number depends on who's counting). Toumaï is the earliest hominid known; the only species of hominid alive today is *Homo sapiens*, the species that includes all humans now living. Hominid fossils are extremely rare, and when they are found at all, they tend to be in a very bad state indeed. Most consist of fragments of tooth enamel, and – if you are lucky – whole teeth. Particularly sharp-eyed fossil-hunters might find a small piece of bone, such as a joint of a finger or toe, or the knobbly end of a limb bone. Rarer still are skulls. These tell us more about the bearer than any other part of the skeleton – and whole skeletons are almost unheard of.

Skulls exert a power that transcends the scientific. A skull is iconic, especially if it has a face. Faces have histories, personalities; this emotional resonance explains why hominid skulls are among the most precious prizes for any fossil-hunter. Given the general rarity of hominids throughout prehistory, the discovery of any fossil hominid skull older than a hundred thousand years or so is a notable event. Until last year, the oldest-known skull was of a creature named *Kenyanthropus platyops* that lived in Kenya around three and a half million years ago. Toumaï took that record and doubled it.

For Michel Brunet, the leader of the expedition, the discovery of Toumaï was the crowning moment of a long career prospecting the desert for fossils. He and his team had been exploring the Djurab desert for more than a decade. They had recovered many beautifully preserved animal bones from a desert moonscape, where once were the luxuriant margins of a predecessor of modern Lake Chad. They had even found a few scraps of a hominid, from a stratum of rock about half the age of the one that finally yielded Toumaï. Coming up to retirement and already the far side of a heart attack, Brunet had claimed his prize.

Unusually for this highly competitive and territorial area of science, Brunet was quick to share his discovery with his academic colleagues. This may reflect the devil-may-care attitude of a scientist coming to the end of his career, who has nothing to lose by generosity. But I think his motivations were more truly scientific. Toumaï was not only a prize, and very ancient, but like nothing before discovered, something quite unexpected and new. Discovery – real discovery, that is, not just incremental addition to the known canon – becomes an encounter with paradox, for it offers something completely unexpected which we must perforce interpret according to the limitations of what we know.

In many ways, Toumaï was as primitive and ape-like as we would expect for something so ancient. At the same time, it had features we'd only otherwise associate with creatures far more advanced. The flat, human-like face and the small, neat teeth were very far from ape-like. Most startling were the immense, shelf-like brow ridges, never seen outside our own relatively recently evolved genus, *Homo*. As any true scientist would be, Brunet was not ashamed to admit perplexity. Rather than keep it all to himself, he took Toumaï on tour, to show him off to fellow students of human evolution and see what they made of it. That's when rumours started to reach me that something special was afoot.

The first I heard was from *Nature*'s West Coast news reporter, Rex Dalton, known as 'Tyrannosaurus' Rex for his tenacious pursuit of a good news lead, especially stories about fossils. In the course of researching a story on the problems of hunting for fossils in Africa, he called on the anthropologist Tim White at the University of California, Berkeley, when Brunet and Toumaï were also in town. Rex didn't say very much – no more than that a French researcher was on to something. In any case, he and I often exchange emails on matters of mutual interest, so I didn't immediately pick up on the significance of what he had to say. More startling was an email a few days later from Bernard Wood, an anthropologist at George Washington University in Washington DC. Professor Wood's manner is always urbane and measured, which made the urgency and excitement of his note all the more arresting. That's when I phoned Brunet (now back in Poitiers) and invited myself to his laboratory.

A few days later, I was in Brunet's office with a plaster cast of Toumaï and a parade of replica skulls of extinct hominids. It was clear that Toumaï was something rather different from all of them. It also looked different from the skulls of gorillas and chimps we had to hand. At that time, Brunet had no firm idea where Toumaï stood in the great scheme of things, and freely admitted as much. He felt it was a hominid, but he could not be absolutely sure that it was not more closely related to chimpanzees, gorillas, or the common ancestry of man and one or other of these modern apes. The clincher would come with the dicovery of lower jaws and teeth, for hominids have a characteristic pattern of wear on the canine teeth, dictated by the manner in which lower and upper teeth meet, or occlude. To check this, he'd need lower jaws, and these had not been found at the study site in Chad.

Then, when he felt that he could take me into his confidence, he took me to a safe in a back office and, with a flourish, showed me the real thing. Taking me and Toumaï down the hall to a large, empty teaching laboratory, he sat me down while he went to take a telephone call. There we were, in a deserted classroom – just me, and the earliest witness to human ancestry. I put the skull down very carefully in case I dropped it.

The next morning, Brunet and I were in a café opposite the railway station waiting for the arrival of Patrick Vignaud, Brunet's chief associate in the expedition. Vignaud had travelled non-stop from Chad via Paris, and when he got off the train, he looked like he'd been sandblasted. Moments later, Brunet and Vignaud saw me to the platform for my homeward connection. It was as I waited for the Paris-bound TGV to pull up that I tried to assess the significance of all I had seen. Clearly, Toumaï was a fossil of immense significance, but precisely how significant was it? I found myself trying to compass the immeasurable. Still mindful of John Maddox's warning against hype, I realized that I would have to judge the significance of Toumaï very nicely, being careful not to overdo it. But what if Toumaï really was that once-in-a-lifetime find that deserved the label of 'major breakthrough'? In an age of spin and hype, how do you avoid the accusation of crying wolf? And how, I asked myself, do people judge the ultimate, historical importance of great events in which they were themselves involved?

When confronted with such a dilemma, scientists achieve perspective through comparison. Brunet tried to place Toumaï in the human story by comparing it with skulls of modern apes and extinct hominids already known. Perhaps, I thought, the significance of historical events might be assessed in the same way. I wondered about discoveries in the past that shared the same circumstances as those attending Toumaï – discoveries of fossils that defied comparison with anything then known. The significance of such finds would, of course, have been validated by the passage of time, and might provide a yardstick against which I could rate Toumaï's importance. I had the answer after a few moments' thought.

In 1924, a scientist called Raymond Dart at the University of the Witwatersrand in South Africa received a fossil skull that had been blasted out of a limestone quarry at a place called Taungs in the Transvaal. The fossil was the complete face and the natural cast of the brain of a small, ape-like creature. Examining the fossil closely, Dart realized that it had belonged to a small child, but of no species then known, living or extinct. It was too small to have been human; and yet it did not seem to have resembled the skull of an ape, either. Realizing the implications of the find, Dart took the exceptionally bold step of describing the fossil as a kind of halfway house, an 'ape-man'. He called it *Australopithecus africanus*, 'the Southern Ape of Africa', but the title of the paper eventually published in *Nature* (in February 1925) made his intentions absolutely clear. The new find was 'The Man-Ape of South Africa'.

The immediate reaction of the scientific establishment was cool. Dart was a relative unknown, working in a distant part of the world not hitherto associated with this kind of discovery. Although Darwin had speculated that clues to human origins might be found in Africa, there were as yet few tangible signs of our ancient heritage in that continent. Indeed, Africa had yielded but one specimen bearing on the question, a relatively modern-looking skull found in 1921 at Broken Hill, in what is now Zambia.

Most of the little evidence there was concerning human evolutionary history came from Europe and Asia. The first remains of Neanderthal man, that quintessential caveman, were found in Germany in 1856 (although a skull, discovered in Gibraltar some decades earlier, has since been assigned to the Neanderthals). But Neanderthals were so similar to modern humans that some anthropologists refused to believe that they represented a different species from modern humans. Their anatomy gave no clear clues about humanity's kinship (if any) with apes.

Another find, *Pithecanthropus erectus* (later renamed *Homo erectus*) from Java, was also relatively modern in aspect – far more so than *Australopithecus*. Indeed, at least one of the finest minds of the age speculated that the origin of humanity might lie in Asia, and not Africa. That mind belonged to Henry Fairfield Osborn, Director of the American Museum of Natural History in New York. Between 1921 and 1930, Osborn commissioned a series of expeditions to Mongolia with the explicit brief of bringing back evidence for human ancestry. Those missions were famous for two things: one was their charismatic and resourceful leader, Roy Chapman Andrews, the real-life prototype for Indiana Jones. The second was their rich haul of discoveries – of dinosaurs, dinosaur nests and dinosaur eggs. But not one scrap of hominid.

And then, of course, there was Piltdown Man. This fossil of a very modern-looking skull associated with an ape-like jaw had been discovered in southern England in 1912 and set the tone for the next thirty or forty years of anthropological thinking. Based on the Piltdown skull, scientists thought that the first feature of modern humanity to emerge was a large brain. Piltdown was exposed as a fraud in the early 1950s – the skull really had come from a modern human, the jaw from an orang-utan, artificially aged to look like real fossils. But when Dart made his discovery, nobody doubted that Piltdown Man was genuine.

In the context of the times, it is easy to see why the Taungs child was dismissed. The small brain – so much smaller than Piltdown – suggested that it was far more ape than Man. Its location, far away from the areas then thought to have been most important for human evolution, also counted against it. In Taungs, the scientific establishment found itself confronted with something so far beyond expectation that it felt disinclined to accept it as the world-shaking discovery it patently was. But extraordinary claims require extraordinary evidence, and many felt that Dart had simply not provided that evidence. The correspondence columns of issues of *Nature* subsequent to the announcement were full of detailed (and, in hindsight, somewhat patronizing) put-downs of the find, belittling the fossil – and the man who found it.

Things changed when Robert Broom, another scientist based in South Africa, sought out Dart and the Taungs skull, and wrote to *Nature* vouching for its authenticity as a genuinely new thing. Broom went on to discover a whole series of fossils of ape-men from southern Africa, showing that Dart's report was no fluke. Some of these finds were thought to represent the adults of *Australopithecus africanus*, showing that it really was a kind of intermediate between apes and Man. Yet further finds were of different species of extinct hominid. In the end, the scientific panjandrums of London had to accept that Dart had been right after all.

A few years later, an entrepreneurial son of a missionary to the Kikuyu tribe of Kenya started finding similar ape-men in the Rift Valley of East Africa. His name was Louis Leakey, father of an illustrious dynasty of fossil-hunters. Largely because of the efforts of Broom and Leakey, the world now knows that the interval between the divergence of the hominid family from that of the apes, and the appearance of the genus *Homo*, was a very long one – perhaps millions of years – and the stage for this long prehistory was very largely African. The interval was populated with a variety of hominids, all now extinct. *Australopithecus africanus* was just one of these. In hindsight, the announcement of the 'Man-Ape of South Africa' stands a milestone in the history of anthropology, marking the time when a single, new discovery opened up huge and hitherto unexpected vistas of possibility.

It struck me that the story of Dart and the Taungs child bore many similarities with the tale of Brunet and Toumaï, more than seventy-five years later. First, there is Michel Brunet himself. He is well known and respected in the small community of anthropologists, but – like Raymond Dart – he is hardly a household name. Second, Brunet has tended to work in places remote from the anthropological action. Convinced that West Africa has a story to tell, he has stayed away from the fossil-bearing localities of eastern and southern Africa pioneered by Broom and the Leakeys. To discover a hominid of pivotal importance in Chad is, in its way, as unexpected now as finding one in southern Africa back in the 1920s. Third, like the Taungs child, the fossil of Toumaï presents a mixture of ancient and modern that both challenges and defies interpretation. All this reasoning explains why I chose my hype carefully, selling this fossil as the most important find of its kind 'in living memory' – that is, since Dart and *Australopithecus africanus*.

Some weeks after my return, Brunet's team discovered jaws to go with the skull. This new discovery sent Brunet and Toumaï on another round of tours; to Zurich, where the machines exist that could X-ray the jaws with sufficient clarity and resolution to image the finest details of the roots of the teeth (the details of tooth roots being very important in judgements of humanity); and to the National Museums of Kenya in Nairobi, where the fossil could be compared with the peerless collection of East African fossils discovered by the Leakeys and their colleagues.

The result of all this activity convinced Brunet and his colleagues that Toumaï was a hominid.

In due course, Brunet and Vignaud submitted a pair of papers to *Nature*. Brunet headed the team whose paper described Toumaï in the formal language of science, whereas the paper from Vignaud and his associated team detailed the rich and hitherto poorly known geology of the Djurab desert.

After detailed scrutiny by a panel of independent referees – again, all part of the deliberations of scientific publication – the paper was published on Thursday 11 July 2002. *Nature* is always published on a Thursday, and we felt the closest Thursday to Bastille Day (14 July) was fitting, given the potentially revolutionary character of the findings. And Toumaï quickly set the world's media alight in a way that is enjoyed by very few scientific discoveries. When pictures of the skull started appearing in cartoons in newspapers such as the *Guardian* ('Pensions Advice from Man's Oldest Relative' by the ever-acerbic Steve Bell) and magazines such as *Private Eye* ('Was this the World's First Tory?' by the pseudonymous Miss I.N.G. Link) I realized that Toumaï had penetrated the popular consciousness like no other science story I'd known.

Hot on the heels of the story came a very public intervention by some of Brunet's critics (with their own fossil hominid to champion), denouncing the find as a 'female gorilla'. This added spice to the tale – and confirmed me in my view that I'd been right to compare Toumaï with Taungs: the critics had adopted the same arguments and language with respect to Toumaï as a different chorus of critics had done with the Taungs skull a lifetime earlier.

So what, precisely, is so important about Toumaï? What's all the fuss about? I can think of two things that make Toumaï the discovery of a lifetime, rather than just the story of the year. The first has to do with timing: Toumaï is the first significant find from a period of time thought to be crucial in human evolution about which we have hitherto known next to nothing. Ten million years ago, the world was full of fossil apes of every kind. However, there is little consensus on which of these apes lies closest to our own ancestry. Five million years ago we start to pick up fossils of the first hominids – to be sure, only scraps of bone and fragments of teeth, but just enough to say that the human lineage was well established.

But the interval between ten and five million years ago is the darkest of all dark ages. Only a few scraps of bone – possibly hominid, or possibly not – is all the evidence we have for the existence of perhaps thirty thousand generations of our ancestors. In the past two years, discoveries in Ethiopia and Kenya have chipped away at the top end of this dark period, but some of these finds are debatable, and all are fragmentary. Right into the middle of this factual desert parachutes Toumaï, not a fragment, but a whole skull; something that can give us the first glimpse of what our earliest ancestors looked like, not long after the hominid and chimpanzee lineages diverged. Skulls are goldmines of information that will keep anthropologists happy for decades. Toumaï is like a rainstorm after a decade of drought.

The second thing is that once you start to look at Toumaï, he (Brunet is convinced he's a 'he') just gets odder and odder. He does not represent what you might think of as a missing link, that is, with a smooth gradation of features, as if caught in the act of morphing from ape to human. On the contrary, he looks like a piebald pantomime horse of features thrown together, some extremely primitive as you'd expect, others disconcertingly modern, and still others never before encountered in any hominid (and before you ask, no, he's not a Piltdown-style forgery). This is not the place for a demonstration of the finer points of anatomy, but the implications of such a style of skull are breathtaking. It could be that Toumaï represents just the first-known example of a burst of evolution around six or seven million years ago that produced a variety of creatures, some ape-like, others more human-like, yet others something in between. Out of this melee only hominids and chimps survived to the present day. This could mean, of course, that Toumaï represents something wholly strange and remote by the lights of the present day. While Toumaï is closer to humans than to chimps, this is a bit like saying that Auckland is closer to London than Dublin.

Like *Australopithecus africanus* in 1925, the effect of Toumaï will be to raise the game, to effect a fundamental change in the way we look at human ancestry. At root, the lesson of Toumaï is a Copernican one. Just when we thought we had a good working idea of how hominid ancestry was supposed to work, we are vouchsafed a tiny glimpse of a much larger, grander and more complicated picture of evolution than we'd ever imagined possible.

Scramjets:
the wind beneath their wings

JONATHAN GLANCEY

After one hundred years of flight, air travel is
due a revolution.

'Houston, Tranquillity Base here. The Eagle has landed.' 20 July 1969.
Less than 66 years after Orville Wright took off into an Atlantic wind
blowing over the wide open sands at Kitty Hawk, North Carolina, Neil
Armstrong and Buzz Aldrin had made it all the way to the moon in their
tiny, two-man module. And, no, there was no wind there: the Stars and
Stripes you see in the famous photographs looked as if it was unfurling
in a breeze, but this was because Aldrin was unable to extend it fully.
The flag was meant to hang straight. It did look good 'flapping', but
this illusion was to give rise to conspiracy theories suggesting the whole
lunar operation was nothing more than an elaborate NASA hoax.
Unlike Orville Wright on 17 December 1903, Aldrin and Armstrong
had been earthbound.

1895 'Heavier-than-air flying machines are impossible'

William Thomson, Lord Kelvin, physicist, mathematician and president of the British Royal Society

1908 'We'd like to think all our predictions will prove right. But the highways of history are littered with wrong calls, false insights and bad guesses. Here's a sampler of 20th-century futurology that flopped: I confess that in 1901, I said to my brother Orville that man would not fly for fifty years... Ever since, I have distrusted myself and avoided all predictions'

Wilbur Wright, US aviation pioneer

1911 'Airplanes are interesting toys but of no military value'

Marshal Ferdinand Foch, French military strategist and future World War I commander

1921 'Professor Goddard does not know the relation between action and reaction and the need to have something better than a vacuum against which to react. He seems to lack the basic knowledge ladled out daily in high schools'

New York Times editorial about Robert Goddard's revolutionary rocket work

1926 'This foolish idea of shooting at the moon is an example of the absurd length to which vicious specialization will carry scientists working in thought-tight compartments'

W. A. Bickerton, professor of physics and chemistry at Canterbury College, Christchurch, New Zealand

1956 'Space travel is utter bilge'

Richard van der Riet Wooley, British Astronomer Royal

1976 'I consider it unlikely that the first community in space will be established before 1990, and also unlikely that it will be delayed for another 15 years, to the year 2005'

Gerard O'Neill, The High Frontier

It was no trick. Within a biblical lifespan – threescore years and ten – the Wright Brothers 12hp 'Flyer' had evolved into a spacecraft capable of taking humans to another planet. This was evolution in one direction; but there was another. On 9 February 1969, Jack Wadell, senior Boeing test pilot, took off from Paine Field, Everett, Washington state, in a brand new aircraft that was to revolutionize passenger flight. His mount was the Boeing 747, the 400-plus seater, twin-deck airliner with a range of 5,500 miles.

Almost from the beginning powered aircraft flew in these two directions. The first headed into the realm of magic, dreams and poetry, of heroism, Bleriot, Alcock and Brown, Biggles, Lindbergh, Amelia Earhart, Marina Raskova, St-Exupéry, 'Chuck' Yeager… the right stuff. It would lead us ever faster, higher, further above troposphere, stratosphere, mesosphere, thermosphere, onwards and upwards above the Earth's gravitational pull into star-spangled space.

This was the stuff of nineteen-year-old Pilot Officer John Gillespie Magee Jr's lyrical poem 'High Flight' (1941):

> I've chased the shouting wind along, and flung
> My eager craft through footless halls of air.
> Up, up the long, delirious burning blue
> I've topped the windswept heights with easy grace
> Where never lark, or even eagle flew.
> And, while with silent, lifting mind I've trod
> The high untrespassed sanctity of space,
> Put out my hand, and touched the face of God.

This young American pilot met his maker in a Royal Canadian Air Force Spitfire in 1941. His was, at least in part, the stuff, too, of Yeats's ice-cold 'An Irish Airman foresees his Death' (1922), written in memory of Major Gregory, who flew for the sake of flying against Germans he did not hate for the British he did not love:

> Nor law, nor duty bade me fight,
> Nor public men, nor cheering crowds,
> A lonely impulse of delight
> Drove to this tumult in the clouds.

Amelia
Earhart:
in June 1928,
she became
the first
woman to
fly across
the Atlantic.

This first direction was a thing of terrible beauty, ineffable sorcery, chariots of fire – an invitation on uncertain wings into the realm of eternal and unforgiving sky-gods.

The second direction, the stuff of our everyday lives, was decidedly more prosaic, although no less intriguing. It started, perhaps, with the Douglas DC3, the first recognizably modern and comfortable airliner, in 1935, but more specifically with the Boeing 707, when this sleek airliner began to cross the Atlantic with regular ease in 1958. From then on, although no European would have known or admitted it at the time, Boeing was making the going: 'If it ain't a Boeing, I ain't going.' Boeing, although not alone, was making flying sewing-machine smooth, ticking away hours spent cruising the world's airwaves with the sure action of a Swiss-made quartz watch. This, though, was to become the stuff not of epic poetry, but of a new form of curt prose, an international interrogative spoken not by thundering sky-gods and jutting-jawed heroes, but by patronizing sky-nannies:

'Any wine at all with the meal, sir/madam?'
'Red or white?'
'Chicken or fish?'
'Can you put your seat in the upright position for me, sir/madam?'

And, if not these obligatory lines, then the smooth assurances of captains and first officers reciting professional pilot mantras concerning outside air-temperatures, height above sea level, and polite commands to fasten safety-belts the moment a Boeing, or Boeing lookalike, encounters ripples of air threatening to upset the food and coffee stinking in the seat next to you. This is the world of aircraft, ever quieter, bigger and easier on fuel, never quite seen, but only glimpsed from those giant out-of-town shopping malls that double up as airports; vast machines attached to umbilical cords through which passengers shuffle in various states of nonchalance, boredom, irritation and fear; aircraft that fly with window blinds drawn firmly down in daylight so that the face of God is blotted out by those of soupy Hollywood actors on blurry video screens. Or else, the magic of flight is dispersed by children glued to mind-numbing computer games.

In less than 66 years, the aircraft took us up one flight path to the moon, and along a second to planet 'red or white?' Poetry on the port wing, doggerel to starboard.

The point of the airliner, however, was to get more and more people from A to B, and eventually from A to Z, ever more cheaply. That mechanical sky-god, Concorde, for all its thundering magnificence and technical mastery, was always going to be a supersonic sideshow. Subsonic was the safe, profitable and popular way to fly, with its promise of worldwide meetings, conferences, assignations and 'cheap holidays', as Johnny Rotten once memorably put it in song, 'in other peoples' misery'. Today's 'no frills' airlines with their fleets of Boeing 737s – Ford Transits with wings – are airborne delivery services. Passengers are parcels. Soon enough, many of the flights on these economy runs will be free of charge, the cost included in hotel bills, or footed by cities keen to attract visitors with wallets wide open. Only determined celebs will continue to fork out for first-class tickets on traditional airlines in the hope of being photographed for the tabloids or of sitting next to some bespoke-suited plutocrat who might sign their next improbable deal.

Concorde or jumbo jet: winged horses for courses. How did it happen?

How did powered flight come to be so ordinary – despite its extraordinary nature, its bravura technical achievement – and so very quickly? A century on from the Wright brothers, powered flight is seen, for the most part, as a chore to be endured, a fug of fetid, low-pressure air, crippling seats, medical phobias, permanently engaged lavatories, backrests thrust into your face, stupefying airline magazines, food you would never dream of eating on terra firma, decor adapted as if from a high-street branch of a building society; these, and the occasional, hard-won view of gloriously mutating skies, of cumulus clouds passing like fantastic white galleons, stratocirrus whipping overhead like unbottled genies, of frost sparkling in infinite patterns on tiny aircraft windows, of boats bobbing on green seas far below, of another aircraft darting like some sudden arrow above your own: each a glimpse and gone forever. For a few moments, it is just possible to capture the dream of aviators who took their improbable machines alone across violent seas and eventually up and through the sound barrier (Chuck Yeager in the Bell-X1 in 1947) towards the arc where atmosphere becomes outer space and conventional aircraft will, like Icarus, fall to earth.

The 'red or white?' factor was catapulted forward by World War II. Crossing the Atlantic, the Americans brought with them – along with Hershey bars, chewing gum, swing, Coke, Jeeps and the idea of 'cool' – aircraft that were easy to manufacture, rock-steady in flight and all but unburstable. The 'Flying Fortress' that took the war in broad daylight to Germany was a Boeing, so too its successor, the pressurized 'Superfortress' that dropped atomic bombs on Nagasaki and Hiroshima. Robust US fighters – Mustangs, Thunderbolts, Lightnings – escorted Boeing bombers to and from their targets. British and German fighters seemed almost fey in comparison; glorious machines designed like pedigree racehorses fighting alongside sturdy American hunters, they were bred for the sprint rather than a long day in the saddle.

It was, though, despite the relentless success of US mass-production know-how, hard for Europeans to let go of such craft-based engineering. In the Korean War, piston-engined British Hawker Sea Furys fought a new generation of Soviet and Chinese MiG-15 jets. The Sea Fury, which served in front-line, carrier-borne service with the Fleet Air Arm from 1947 to 1953, remains a fine, subtle machine, winning American air-races even today. It is powered by a Bristol rotary engine of haunting beauty and daunting complexity. By comparison, the much faster MiG-15 was a

Red or white, chicken or fish... and the occasional,
hard-won view of gloriously mutating skies.

rather stunted beast – a pig that really could fly – powered by a metal
tube containing as few moving parts as possible.

Once, but only once, a Sea Fury knocked a MiG-15 from the sky.
It might have been the more exquisite of the two planes, but its day was
all but done. It would, in today's terms, be like driving a Le Mans-winning,
1950s D-type Jaguar to work everyday instead of a modern, air-
conditioned sports car. The Sea Fury, the last of a breed, was a romantic,
refined, hands-on machine. The tough little MiG was a feisty, successful,
mass-produced brat. It was not hard to guess which one would win in
the end, not in terms of the outcome of the Korean War perhaps, but
in the wider theatre of aviation, military and otherwise. There is, though,
a fascinating coda to the Sea Fury story: the last action by one of these
planes, built in Kingston-upon-Thames, Surrey, was over the Bay of Pigs
at the time of the abortive US-backed invasion of Cuba in 1961. It was
a Cuban Air Force Sea Fury that sunk the American supply ship and
gave Castro the advantage he needed.

The romance of flight, however, lives on in a world of Boeings and
Airbuses that look like Boeings, through gliders, balloons, birds, bats,
dragon-flies, model planes and light aircraft. And, in the guise of the
Terrier Mk70 HyShot Scramjet, launched successfully from Woomera
in the South Australian wilderness on 30 July 2002. This air-breathing,
supersonic combustion ramjet may yet allow commercial airliners to fly

at up to ten times the speed of sound, bringing Sydney within 90 minutes of London. And, if this sounds about as commercially intelligent in the age of no-frills, no right-stuff flying as a second-generation Concorde, fasten your seat belts for a moment…

If successful, the Scramjet could yet revolutionize the launch of small space payloads, such as communications satellites, by substantially lowering costs while increasing safety. The engine breathes oxygen from the atmosphere rather than guzzling heavy payloads of dangerous liquid-oxygen that have weighed down space rockets to date. It should, in theory, be easy to maintain: not only is the Scramjet lighter than a conventional rocket, its engine has no moving parts.

A Scramjet-powered aircraft could – a little more theory – take off from Heathrow, stop to pick up at Sydney before flying all the way, and in one single piece, to dock with spacestations or rendezvous with other spacecraft. It could power spaceliners to the moon. Remember the Concorde-like Pan-American spaceliner in Kubrick's *2001: A Space Odyssey*? That seemed a far-off dream a year before Armstrong and Aldrin stepped foot on the moon; the first successful flight of the Scramjet puts it within the realm of possibility. After three decades of 'chicken or fish' flying, aircraft seem thrilling again.

But – keep a tight hold on your throttle – the first flight of the Scramjet lasted just ten minutes, and it was only in the final seconds that the machine went hypersonic. This was, if you like, a twenty-first-century replay of the Wright Brothers' first, brief, powered flight in December 1903. Orville's flew just 120ft – he could have taken off and landed within the length of the economy section of a new Boeing 747-400, which can fly something like 7500 miles between refills. In other words, these are early days for the Scramjet. Given current levels of investment, Australian scientists working at Woomera say, it will be decades before we can take off in '2001'-style spaceliners. It will in any case take a long time to develop the two sets of engines such a machine would need to have one cutting in and out of the other smoothly and safely. To punch into action, a Scramjet engine needs to be scything through the air faster than Mercury or Pegasus; it is only at very high speed that it can start to function independently, and so shoot our imaginary spaceliner into the lightning-bolt world of hypersonic flight.

If we ever get there, though, it is easy to see how a dramatic new technological development might soon enough go the way of 'red or white', 'chicken or fish'. Slyly, Kubrick showed us how the sorcery of space flight might quickly become as boring and as routine as commuting to the office, even though the machinery itself would be soaring into infinite, numinous space. The interior of the Pan-American space Concorde that featured memorably in his 'Odyssey' was satirically bland. A VIP scientist passenger sucked at glum food served by dolly-bird space-stewardesses. The pretentiously uniformed captain and first officer had nothing to do but smile toothpaste smiles and monitor computer displays while the machine flew itself.

Outside, though, the spaceliner was shown to be pirouetting through a majestic backdrop of stars, moon and rotating spacestation accompanied by Strauss's weightless 'Blue Danube Waltz'. The beauty, poetry and wizardry of flight, of air and space travel, Kubrick implied, would be ever further removed as humans learned to live passive, strapped-in, 'red or white' lives.

I was asked to give a talk about flight to primary schoolchildren from very mixed and very poor backgrounds in a city school. I took a sheaf of paper and asked them to make paper aeroplanes and throw them at me. Only a handful knew how to make one. I made a show-off plane that looped-the-loop. An eight-year-old boy, almost impressed, said 'Oi, mister, how did you program it?' But, by the end of the class, they were all flying planes that needed no help from a computer, just a little basic human skill and a delight in flight. I couldn't help thinking that a century of flight in which Major Gregory, John Gillespie Magee Jr, Amy Johnson, Marina Raskova, 'Chuck' Yeager and Neil Armstrong have played their fleeting parts, has been as long as it has taken us to get from the *Flyer's* first, unsure, twelve-second hop to the certainty of twelve steady hours, and even more, of 'chicken or fish'.

Biodiversity and the case of the missing lynx

MARK COLLINS AND ADRIAN NEWTON

Wilderness areas are being destroyed, so why do we think it doesn't affect us?

Johannesburg, South Africa, 4 September 2002: Today world leaders agreed targets to alleviate poverty, make sustainable development a reality and wisely manage humankind's everyday essentials: water, energy, health, agriculture and biodiversity.

Excuse me, biodiversity? What is that exactly and why is it an everyday essential? Correspondents worldwide reach for their dictionaries: 'The variability among living organisms from all sources including, *inter alia*, terrestrial, marine and other aquatic ecosystems, and the ecological complexes of which they are part; this includes diversity within species, between species and of ecosystems.' Right. So, are the world's poor going to beat poverty by eating beetles and harvesting berries from wildlands? Haven't we spent the last ten thousand years trying to get away from dependence on nature?

In 2002 it was thirty years since the world's first major commitment to the environment in Stockholm. Ten years since the Earth Summit at Rio adopted the Convention on Biological Diversity. But biodiversity is still stuck in the category 'interesting but not part of my daily concerns'. Ask any passer-by on the street what he or she understands by water, energy, health and agriculture and you can expect a solid answer in any language. But the term biodiversity would elicit blank looks from many, concerns about pandas and tigers from a few, and a scattering of quotes about football-field-sized rainforests being cut down.

We have Kofi Annan and the United Nations to thank for adding biodiversity to the list of issues discussed at the World Summit on Sustainable Development in Johannesburg. Building on concepts in the Millennium Declaration and the linked Millennium Development Goals, the UN is emphasizing that biodiversity – and the ecosystem functions that are an integral part of biodiversity (like soil, water and climate management) – underpin all our basic needs, and should lie at the heart of any human development programme.

The 2002 United Nations Environment Programme (UNEP) paper, 'A Framework for Action on Biodiversity and Ecosystem Management', published for the Johannesburg summit, emphasized the value of the natural world. Healthy ecosystems and biological agents keep our waters clean. The Earth's climate and energy systems depend upon balanced interactions between forests, the seas and the atmosphere. Our health depends upon pharmaceuticals derived from nature's chemistry set, and our agriculture is based upon the genetic diversity of just a few dozen species. And we should remember that the world's 307 million people who survive on less than a dollar a day (rising to 420 million by 2017) live even closer to nature. They depend directly on wild species to deal with waste, deliver medicines, feed and clothe the kids, provide shelter from the weather and generally balance the family budget.

This year the evidence that our planet is experiencing the greatest die-off of plants and animals since the demise of the dinosaurs grew stronger. More than 800 species are known to have become extinct during the last 500 years, but in 2002 new assessments indicated how the global extinction crisis is deepening. The 'red list' produced by the IUCN – The World Conservation Union – listed 11,167 species now under threat, including a quarter of all mammals and one in eight bird species. Not surprisingly, it is the warmer countries that have most to lose. Indonesia, India, Brazil and China are among the countries with the most threatened mammals and birds, while plant species are declining rapidly in South and Central America, Central and West Africa, and Southeast Asia.

Many charismatic animals of direct or indirect economic value are among those in decline. The UNEP-led 'Great Apes Survival Project' (GrASP) is concerned that Bornean orang-utans, for example, now number fewer than 15,000 in the wild, having been reduced from around 250,000 individuals at the beginning of the twentieth century. Tourists hoping for a glimpse of one of our nearest relatives are unlikely to spend their dollars visiting a landscape of burnt stumps. The saiga, a migratory antelope inhabiting the steppes of Central Asia and once an important source of protein and skins, has declined from over 1 million in 1993 to fewer than 50,000 animals remaining today. In India populations of vultures that once performed important sanitation services have declined by more than 90 per cent in ten years, leading to widespread impacts on ecology and human health.

Don't be deceived into believing this is a developing-country problem. In Spain and Portugal the Iberian lynx is on the verge of becoming the first wild cat to go extinct for at least two thousand years, numbers having dropped to less than half of the 1200 individuals known in the early 1990s. In the UK, over the past twenty years, most common farmland bird species have declined by almost half, including the skylark, song thrush and linnet. Rarities like the red-backed shrike, corncrake and cirl bunting have fared worse still and disappeared from large areas.

Some say that the coming and going of species is a natural phenomenon. True, more than 95 per cent of the species that have ever existed on Earth are no longer with us. But even if you are bold or foolhardy enough to forgo the option of sharing our planet with rhinos, pandas and giant redwoods, the effect may not be as simple as you think. The main cause of species loss is physical degradation and destruction of ecosystems, and pollution of habitats with chemicals and alien invasive species. These habitat impacts affect 89 per cent of all threatened birds, 83 per cent of mammals, and 91 per cent of threatened plants. Are we so blind as to think it does not affect us as well? Future generations will not be impressed.

It is clear that behind the headlines about endangered species lies an even more significant concern about the degradation and breakdown of Earth's ecological systems. Interference with basic ecological functions like the water, nutrient and carbon cycles, soil development and waste decomposition is fuelling poverty by destroying human development options. Poverty is of course a major cause of global conflict and instability – and we will all be the poorer if these links are not recognized.

We now divert about 40 per cent of the Earth's productivity to our own ends – and waste a lot of it in the process. Human numbers continue to grow; by more than 2 billion during the past thirty years. Faced with the relentless expansion of urban centres, agriculture and the harvesting of natural resources like fish and timber, it's no wonder that our tiny investments in the environment have resulted mainly in words and good intentions rather than measurable achievements.

The endangered orang-utan. A quarter of all mammals and one bird species in eight are under threat.

The 2002 *World Atlas of Biodiversity*, from UNEP's World Conservation Monitoring Centre (WCMC), cites the continuing clearance of tropical forests for agriculture as the largest single factor responsible for biodiversity loss at the global scale. Other important ecosystems are also being damaged at an alarming rate. Freshwaters are particularly vulnerable, with around half of the world's rivers now seriously depleted or polluted – let's hope that the 2003 UN International Year of Freshwaters can help. The marine environment is also of growing concern. Fish stocks, for example cod in the North Sea, are collapsing from over-exploitation. In 2002 coral reefs suffered another bleaching event, notably on the Great Barrier Reef, where up to 90 per cent of corals were killed in places. A rise in sea temperature linked to climate change was to blame, a further worry for the WCMC-based International Coral Reef Action Network. Forests, freshwaters, coral reefs – these are important to humans too. Forests produce the oxygen we breathe and absorb the carbon dioxide that is changing our climate. Freshwaters irrigate our agriculture, drive hydroelectricity plants and are a vital resource for people everywhere. And coral reefs protect many islands and coastlines from the destructive force of the sea. We can't afford to lose them.

Conserving species doesn't necessarily mean protecting pristine environments. Most European wildlife has adapted to a mosaic of farming, forestry, quarrying and golf courses. But the recent declines in farmland bird populations experienced in the UK are also occurring throughout north-west Europe, largely because the intensification of agriculture leaves no pickings for wild species. The appropriate management of farmland represents perhaps the most important conservation challenge faced in Britain. However, it is likely that other major losses of biodiversity are occurring that we know little about. Birds are simply the group of organisms for which most information is available.

In 2002, the thirty-year-old UN Environment Programme wrote a state-of-the-environment review, the Global Environment Outlook (GEO-3), and didn't like what it found. Extensive areas of land have been laid waste through inappropriate human activity. In the Asia and Pacific region, increases in irrigation have resulted in salinization of 25–30 million hectares. In total, 2 billion hectares of soil, equal to an area bigger than the United States and Mexico combined, is now classed as degraded because of overgrazing, deforestation and agricultural over-intensification.

Such environmental degradation can have enormous economic costs. India is losing more than $10 billion annually, or 4.5 per cent of its gross domestic product, because of it. Declining environmental quality is also a cause of rising health risks. Sewage pollution of the sea has caused a health crisis in many areas. For example, eating contaminated shellfish now causes 2.5 million cases of infectious hepatitis annually, resulting in 25,000 deaths and a further 25,000 people suffering long-term disability owing to liver damage. The global economic impact of marine contamination, in terms of human disease and ill health, is thought to be running at nearly $13 billion annually. The bottom line is that loss of species and wildlands is a clear indicator of a more general decline in the quality of the environments in which we live, and on which we depend. The miner's canary is warning us of trouble ahead.

But it's not all bad news. There have been some positive environmental trends over the past thirty years. Major improvements in river and air quality have been achieved in areas of North America and Europe. Efforts to control the hunting of whales have allowed some populations to recover. The Montreal Protocol appears to be helping the repair of the ozone hole – a threat to the health of many species, including our own. A particularly optimistic headline statistic can be found in the growth in total extent of protected areas, such as national parks, which have more than quadrupled from 2.78 million square kilometres in 1970 to 12.18 million square kilometres in 2000. Many of these sites are proving successful at stopping land clearances, and to a lesser extent at tackling issues such as logging, hunting, fires and grazing pressures. In the seas the level of protection is much less, a point noted at Johannesburg where leaders set new targets for marine parks.

Given the success in establishing almost 10 per cent of the land surface as protected areas, one wonders why the number of threatened species continues to rise so inexorably. In 2003, the IUCN will convene the World Parks Congress, a jamboree of park planners and managers that takes place every ten years and is intended to grapple with this problem. Admittedly large areas are accounted for in ice-bound Greenland and Antarctica, and in the barren sands of the Middle East, but issues of park-management effectiveness may lie behind performance problems in many areas.

The GEO-3 report tells us we are at a crossroads in terms of our future impact on the planet and the goods and services it can provide for our future. Decisions taken today will define the kind of environment that this and future generations will enjoy. We have a choice between a future driven predominantly by market forces or a future involving far-reaching changes in values, lifestyles, policies and cooperation between all sectors of society.

Forecasts based on current trends suggest that in thirty years' time, if unregulated market forces predominate, over 70 per cent of the Earth's land surface will be affected by the impact of roads, mining, cities and other infrastructure developments. Impacts on ecosystem functions will be severe: more than 55 per cent of the global human population will be short of water, and more than 70 per cent of forests will have been felled, affecting climate, soil erosion and many other variables. Losses of species diversity are likely to be particularly severe in Southeast Asia, the Congo basin and parts of the Amazon, where as much as 48 per cent of the area could become converted to agriculture, plantations and urban areas by 2032.

For all the press criticism, world leaders in Johannesburg made a bold decision in agreeing to significantly reduce the loss of biodiversity by the year 2010. At this point they don't really know how they are going to do it, or even how to measure their success. Biodiversity remains a backward science, and we need more and better information about the number and types of species on Earth, together with basic information about where they live and how. Perhaps the newly formed Global Biodiversity Information Facility, headquartered in Copenhagen, will provide the answer. We will also need to know a lot more about the ability of the planet to provide the ecological conditions needed to manage our waste and provide us with raw materials for food, fibre and fuel. We are depending upon the Millennium Ecosystem Assessment, a massive UN-led investigation, to give us the answers.

Recent research into the economic reasons for conserving wild nature, published by no fewer than nineteen authors in the journal *Science*, indicates that natural and semi-natural habitats can, if used sustainably, produce one hundred times the economic benefits arising from their conversion to other uses. Examples included tropical forests in Malaysia and Cameroon, mangroves in Thailand, wetlands in Canada and coral reefs in the Philippines. Why is it that decisions are apparently being taken

at all levels to adopt less viable development paths? The answer seems
to be inadequate planning, short-termism and perverse subsidies
that encourage planners to head in the wrong direction.

We must rise to the challenge posed by biodiversity loss and the damage
to ecosystems: the UN and other international and national organizations
need both the mandate to act and the backing to act successfully. That
requires better information and surer understanding. What will happen
if we go on as we are, not just now but in decades or centuries? How will
things change if we change our ways? We need to think about how we
get these complex issues across to the people who think up policies,
the people who decide on those policies, and the people who have
to live with the consequences. We must understand that we depend
on biodiversity, just as surely as we depend on water, energy, health
and agriculture, because biodiversity underwrites all of them.

Stem cells:
life is what you make of it

ARLENE JUDITH KLOTZKO

New medical technologies involving embryo tissue
seem only to raise major new moral questions.

At the very beginning of our becoming is the embryo. Five to seven
days after fertilization – when the embryo is a ball of undifferentiated
cells no larger than a grain of sand – scientists can derive from its inner
cell mass the embryonic stem cell.

Embryonic stem cells can become anything and everything in the
human body: every cell type, every kind of tissue. In the lab, *in vitro*,
scientists can preserve their malleability and their immortality, enabling
them to go on dividing and dividing. Forever young, they are cells
of eternal becoming. A description of their potential for renewal and
transformation seems as suited for recounting in Ovid's *Metamorphoses*
or a fairy tale as it does to science news. But science news it is, and very
good news indeed.

While stem cells can come from an early embryo, foetus or adult, they all have two key properties. Under the right conditions, they have the ability to reproduce themselves for long periods of time – for the life of the organism, in the case of adult stem cells. They can also give rise to the specialized cells that make up the tissues and organs of the body. The vast majority of stem cells are believed to give rise to only a limited number of specialized cell types. Pluripotent stem cells, which can generate all of the cell types in a foetus and in adults, can be derived from two tissue sources: blastocysts (embryos about five to seven days old) and primordial germ cells (ancestors of sperm and eggs).

In 1998, papers were published by two teams of researchers revealing that they had isolated human pluripotent stem cells. James Thomson and his group at the University of Wisconsin-Madison isolated human embryonic stem cells from the inner cell mass of embryos left over after IVF treatment and grew them into five immortal cell lines. John Gearhart and his team at Johns Hopkins University in Baltimore, Maryland, isolated embryo germ cells from the primordial reproductive cells of human foetuses obtained from terminated pregnancies. Following upon the work of Dr Gearhart and Dr Thomson, other researchers have begun to demonstrate the therapeutic potential of mouse and human embryonic stem cells.

Adult stem cells are found throughout the body but not in every organ. They divide as needed to replenish themselves and to produce cells appropriate and specific to their particular context. Somatic cells inevitably die and adult stem cells manufacture their replacements. Although these stem cells are already committed to a specific fate, several recent studies have shown that, in some cases, these commitments can be overridden and that one type of adult stem cell may be capable of being reprogrammed into another type in order to cure disease. This malleability seems to be particularly true with respect to nerve and blood stem cells.

The journal *Science* has likened such a transformation to a music student becoming a successful professional baseball player. This process is rather like the first stages of cloning, in that cells are taught to act in a way that is not natural or normal for them, to alter their course. In contrast, the task before us with respect to embryonic stem cells is harnessing and directing what comes naturally. But it is not going to be easy. And it's going to take time.

Compared with ES (embryonic stem) cells, adult stem cells seem to have very real shortcomings: they are difficult to get at and there are not many of them. A recent paper in *Nature*, by Catherine Verfaillie and her colleagues at the University of Minnesota, identified a very rare type of bone marrow adult stem cell that appears to be perhaps even as versatile as embryonic stem cells, although that seems rather unlikely. Professor Verfaillie advocates strongly that research should continue on embryonic stem cells. The therapeutic promise of her cells is far from clear, and different types of stem cell may be best for different diseases. It is simply too early to say.

Long before the Verfaillie paper was published, the promise of adult stem cells was being hailed by pro-life groups opposed to both abortion and embryo research. The teachings of the Catholic Church also hold that IVF is morally unacceptable as life begins at conception. Since the great majority of the British public do not share these views and the objective was to win the political debate, appeals to ethics and religion were often replaced by appeals to science, or perhaps pseudo-science.

Of course, embryonic stem cell research does raise moral issues – principally the status of the embryo. As Mary Warnock has recently noted, while the question most often posed is when exactly does life begin, that's not the issue at all. The true question that needs to be answered is this: when does the embryo become morally significant?

Prompted by the birth of the first IVF (or 'test tube') baby, Louise Brown, this question was first asked and answered in the UK almost twenty years ago. At last count, the technique developed by Robert Edwards and Patrick Steptoe, working in Cambridge, had given the world a large number of healthy babies who otherwise would never have been born. They also gave the world a new scientific and moral construct – the human embryo in a dish, developing outside the body, to be observed, analysed and manipulated.

Clearly IVF and the embryo research that would be required to develop and improve it posed novel and important ethical and policy issues. These were examined by a commission formed in 1982 and chaired by Mary Warnock. Its report, *A Question of Life*, was issued in 1984. Its conclusions were incorporated into the Human Fertilisation and Embryology Act of 1990 – legislation that regulates embryo research and assisted reproduction with donated gametes. Embryo research was allowed until the fourteenth day, when the beginnings of a nervous system appear in the form of the so-called primitive streak. After fourteen days, twinning becomes impossible, so it can be said that a particular embryo could develop – if implanted – into a unique individual. In vitro fertilization could be performed only in licensed clinics.

The creation of surplus or spare embryos was, and remains, a crucial part of IVF. They could be stored for five years – subsequently extended to ten – and if neither used nor donated for research, they were to be destroyed. Finally, embryos could be created solely for research purposes. During the twelve years that the Act has been in force, just over one hundred research embryos were produced.

In January 2001, the House of Lords voted to allow embryo research for the additional purposes of developing therapies for devastating and currently incurable diseases. The case was made in Parliament on behalf of those who were suffering grievously and could benefit from the research. Their moral claims to be heard and to be helped simply outweighed the case presented by the pro-life campaigners for the absolute sanctity of the very early embryo. Both the Commons and Lords voted overwhelming to allow the research. As far as the embryo is concerned, stem cell research presents no major new ethical issues not already thought through in relation to IVF. The embryonic stem cells will be derived at about the five-day stage – well before the fourteen-day cut-off – from embryos not wanted or needed and thus destined to be destroyed.

The most controversial recommendation of the Warnock Commission, and the most controversial provision of the legislation, concerned the purposeful creation of embryos solely for research and not for reproduction. This was a large ethical leap and many other countries have specifically disallowed it. However, in moving – as Britain has – from creating embryos for research by fertilization to allowing their creation by cell nuclear replacement – so-called therapeutic cloning – the UK has not travelled a great moral distance. There is a strong regulatory framework in Britain to keep the research on the scientific and moral straight and narrow.

Therapeutic cloning is a bit like a Woody Allen script run backwards. In Allen's 1973 film, *Sleeper*, attempts are made to clone a dictator from his preserved nose. Now, instead of cloning people from spare parts, scientists hope to derive those parts – cells, tissues and perhaps, one day, even organs – by taking genetic material from a person and deriving immunologically compatible embryonic stem cells from the resulting embryos. Therapeutic cloning may one day find its place in the clinic, but even if it does not the lessons that can be learned from basic research will be valuable indeed.

At this point, we know of only one way to reprogram the nucleus of an adult (somatic) cell – cloning. The nucleus of that cell is inserted into an egg whose own nucleus has been removed. Factors in the gel-like substance of the egg called the cytoplasm trick the nucleus into behaving like a nucleus of a one-cell embryo. In other words, a cell that only 'knew' how to do or be one thing becomes capable of providing the instructions to construct an entire organism. If the mechanism of this reprogramming can be understood, it may be possible to bypass the embryo stage entirely and convert say the skin cell of Mr Jones, who has Parkinson's disease, into nerve cells that will cure him.

The dominant ethical argument that is made against allowing therapeutic cloning is based on notions of the slippery slope. The idea behind this sort of argument is that if you do x, which is acceptable, you will end up doing y, which is not. Indeed, two types of slippery slope – logical and sociological – exist. On the logical slippery slope, you slide to the bottom and embrace the morally unacceptable because there is no way to distinguish it from an acceptable practice. You can slide down the sociological slippery slope from one practice to another – even if the two are conceptually different – just because the existence of one creates a social climate receptive to the other.

Therapeutic cloning is conceptually distinct from reproductive cloning. Although the first step is the same, the intent behind the practices is not. The former would be done in order to save lives by treating diseases now incurable – say, Parkinson's disease, motor neurone disease, and multiple sclerosis. The latter – creating a person by cloning – would be done for reasons extending from egomania to confusion between replication and resurrection, or perhaps the understandable desire to have a biologically related child. Will therapeutic cloning make it more likely that people come to accept reproductive cloning? I don't think so.

Therapeutic cloning is intended to heal the sick. The cells created through cloning would be an extension of the patient: a means to treat him with cells generated by his own body. It's almost like donating a pint of blood for yourself in case you need it for subsequent surgery. Even though I do not believe in a slippery slope from therapeutic to reproductive cloning, a society's laws should give voice to its values. The ban on reproductive cloning that was rushed through Parliament late last year was a good idea; it erected a legal barrier to prevent a slide towards a practice that is now, and perhaps will always be, unsafe and therefore unethical.

The Human Fertilisation and Embryology Authority has issued licenses for embryonic stem cell research but not for therapeutic cloning – not yet. The UK has not only taken the lead in IVF, ethical reflection and legislation, scientists in this country have also made breakthroughs in two other related areas: mammalian cloning and the derivation of mouse embryonic stem cells. In 1997, a UK team introduced an astonished world to Dolly the sheep, the first mammal to be cloned from a differentiated cell. A dozen years earlier, Steen Willadsen, a Danish scientist working in Cambridge, cloned the first mammal – also a sheep – from an embryonic cell. At the same sort of time, also in Cambridge, Martin Evans and his team derived mouse ES cells and used them to produce 'knockout mice' (so-called because a gene had been knocked out) – the most important model for the study of genetics and disease. Both the Gearhart and Thomson teams in the US developed their methods for culturing stem cell lines by drawing upon Evans's work.

With the announcement, in September 2002, of the world's first stem cell bank, the UK is about to take yet another crucial step. This bank, to be housed in an independent laboratory, will contain both embryonic and adult stem cell lines and be an invaluable resource for scientists working in both the public and private sectors.

In a recent study funded by the Economic and Social Research Council, a survey of public attitudes about science by Cardiff University found a shocking level of ignorance and misinformation about science coexisting with strong negative opinions. 'Worrying' was the word used by 44 per cent of respondents to describe recent developments in biotechnology. In my experience of talking to a broad range of people on both sides of the Atlantic, worries about science involve two broad areas – risk and morality.

People in the US are generally less suspicious of scientists and their motives, and also less risk averse. They are not as quick to see the moral downside of scientific breakthroughs, although cloning has certainly created great alarm. They tend to think of science as an engine for human progress, and biomedical science as a fount of promising treatments and cures. I find the level of distrust in the UK as stunning as it is unwarranted. Every scientist I know strives to do his or her work ethically. Scientists are not asking to be society's conscience; that is not a role they want or, indeed, should have. Science and ethics are everybody's business and they are certainly not naturally antagonistic. With respect to stem cell research, the imperatives of both are the same – clarity, transparency, and accountability in the service of a responsible and determined effort to develop therapies to heal the sick and the suffering.

Dinosaurs: see how they run

TIM RADFORD

They could take the heat, they could stand the cold,
but could they sprint? And did a big bang set them
on a course of growth?

Biomechanically, *Tyrannosaurus rex* had a problem. Mathematically,
the biggest killer in the Cretaceous was not up to speed, according to
two researchers in California. John Hutchinson, of Stanford University,
and Mariano Garcia, of Borg-Warner Automotive, reported in *Nature*
on 28 February 2002 that *T. rex* certainly could not have overtaken a car.
With a top speed of somewhere between 10mph and 25mph, the slavering
biped may not even have been able to run down a bicycle.

The problem is that bulk is its own handicap. Britain's own
biomechanician, R. McNeill Alexander of Leeds University showed
in 1989 that the mere act of running could have injured tyrannosaur
bones. Others surmised that the great predator may have lurked in
ambush, or scavenged, or just taken its time, wary of the awful

consequences – when you weigh six or seven tonnes – of tripping and falling over at high speed.

Hutchinson and Garcia took another approach. They thought about size, weight, posture and the mass of leg muscle needed to run at any useful speed. They came up with a simple mechanical model. Then they looked at the leg muscles on an alligator and a chicken, both distant cousins of dinosaurs. The model predicted that an alligator would need 7.7 per cent of its body mass in the muscles of each hind limb. Alligators do not run, and each hind limb muscle was only 3.6 per cent of total body mass. Chickens, however, do run: their model for a chicken predicted that at least 4.7 per cent of its body mass should be invested in each leg muscle. In reality, the dissected chicken had 8.8 per cent of its body mass in each leg muscle. But the bigger the beast, the more leg-power it needs to get going.

'That's why as animals get really enormous, eventually to support their weight, their muscles have to be bigger and bigger and bigger,' Hutchinson said. 'But as they get bigger, they add more mass. So you run up against a problem as animals grow larger in that they need to be adding more muscle cross-sectional area to support their own weight, but the mere fact of adding that muscle adds weight. Eventually, something's got to give.'

They scaled up a chicken to the mass of *T. rex* – think of a six-tonne Rhode Island red – and calculated that to get up to speed, the giant barnyard fowl would need an impossible 99 per cent of its body mass in each leg muscle. 'A giant chicken could not even walk,' Hutchinson said. Then they started thinking about *T. rex*. To run at 45mph, in a crouched posture, the predator would have needed 43 per cent of its body mass in each leg. To run in an almost straight-legged stance, it still needed 13 per cent of its total body mass in the muscles of each hind limb. This is far more leg-power than any living animal possesses.

'Our model shows that these really fast speeds of 50 miles an hour and probably down to even 25 miles an hour just don't hold up when you really scrutinize them and look at the physics,' Hutchinson says. 'It doesn't make a lot of sense that these animals could go that fast. There's really no good evidence that they could.'

Runners or not, dinosaurs certainly got about. A team from Australia and Alaska used the pages of *Science* on 8 February 2002 to do some head-scratching about the implications of dinosaur fossils in south-eastern Australia and the north slope of Alaska. Continents drift,

Size itself must have proved a handicap for *T. rex.* in the predator stakes.

but even in the Cretaceous the north slope of Alaska was north of latitude 60° N. In south-eastern Australia, along with Cretaceous dinosaur fossils, there was evidence of permafrost, ice wedges and hummocky ground. This they took as evidence that mean annual temperatures were somewhere between minus 6°C and plus 3°C. On the other hand, there were also trees that could certainly not have survived in such cold environments today. 'Dinosaurs were doing quite well in high latitudes in both hemispheres 110 to 65 million years ago,' said Roland Gangloff of the University of Alaska. 'They were well adapted and the evidence is so overwhelming that it cries out to be understood.'

The dinosaurs disappeared at the end of the Cretaceous, 65 million years ago, around the same time as a large asteroid crashed into the planet. But an asteroid or comet may also have switched on the chance to dominate the planet in the first place, according to Paul Olsen and colleagues of Columbia University's Lamont-Doherty Earth Observatory,

Biomechanics

writing in *Science* on 16 May 2002. They studied vertebrate fossils from eighty sites in four ancient rift basins that formed as North America began to split apart from its supercontinent parent 230 to 190 million years ago. Dinosaurs first appeared in the Triassic, but the huge carnivorous theropods that make the running in the movies popped up in a thirty-thousand-year span – no time at all, to a geologist – after a mass extinction on Earth. In the same strata, they found four times as much iridium as might have been expected, and a sudden increase in fern spores. Iridium, like platinum, is rare on Earth but more abundant in the stuff flying about in space. So some asteroid or comet hit the Earth at the end of the Triassic, dusting the landscape with iridium, darkening the skies, disturbing the climate and decimating life on the planet. The ferns would have been the first to colonize the wasteland. In this hypothesis, the dinosaurs would have evolved rapidly to take command at the top of the food chain. They then dominated life on the planet for the next 135 million years, before disappearing in another fireball at the end of the Cretaceous: they went out, so to speak, like a light.

Punning machines

PETER FORBES

Nature's engineers got there before us.

It began with Joseph Paxton taking the module for his Crystal Palace in 1851 from the ribs of the leaf of the giant water lily, *Victoria regia*. D'Arcy Thompson, in his magisterial *On Growth and Form* (1917), pointed up many parallels between engineering and biology. Then came Catseyes (1934) and the product trademarked as Velcro (1955). But 2002 was the year in which biomimetics came of age, with

Joseph Paxton drew a lesson from nature for his design of Crystal Palace.

biomimetics papers invading the general journals such as *Nature* and *Science*, and new journals being set up, including *Nature New Materials*.

Biomimetics is the science and technology of devising useful engineering materials, structures and processes from natural analogues. As a named discipline, it is about ten years old. The spur to biomimetics is that nature has developed materials with properties that to us seem miraculous, such as self-cleaning and self-repair, even self-assembly – the little protein factories inside every cell, for example, if broken up by detergent, will simply reassemble and go about their work afresh when the detergent is removed and their normal chemical environment reconstituted.

For a long time, scientists could only marvel at such feats, without any hope of duplicating them, but advances in biology since the 1960s made the rapprochement between engineering and biology inevitable. The electron microscope revealed the amazingly intricate feats of microengineering perfected by evolution: for example, the phages, little crystalline lunar-landing modules that dock on bacteria, inject their DNA and multiply; and the Bombardier beetle, which mimics the doodlebug's rocket motor by using hydrogen peroxide, a well-known rocket fuel, as the oxidizing agent and propellant as a toxic spray that it uses to deter predators. The chemical structures of complex proteins were decoded and correlations between structure and form as revealed by the electron microscope became possible. Natural materials such as spider silk, mussel glue, bone, tooth enamel, and mother-of-pearl (abalone), all of which potentially have properties in advance of normal engineering materials, began to give up their secrets.

When the techniques involve very fine-scale processes, as they often do, the term nanotechnology is used (nano being the dimension one thousandth smaller than micro; 1 nanometre is 1 billionth of a metre). The smart materials produced by these techniques generally do not require the high temperatures, pressures, and corrosive chemicals required by traditional materials manufacturing techniques. In use, they are more efficient than traditional materials. The present trickle of commercial products will turn into a flood over the next twenty years.

There is so much work currently riding under the biomimetics banner on every conceivable substance, but one way of getting a fix on the subject is to distinguish between biomimetics proper and bio-inspiration. Biomimetics would include hydrofoils that swim like fish, using undulations from shape-memory bending elements, or attempts to manufacture spider silk in industrial quantities, or mussel glue that sets underwater, or tiny robot planes that fly with flapping wings like insects. Bio-inspiration is mostly found in the burgeoning world of materials science. It is nature's assembly techniques that give rise to the materials' special properties. Technologists would like to use similar strategies to fabricate electronics components and high-performance composites. The great bulk of studies currently under way are, strictly, bio-inspired rather than biomimetic.

How do nature's fabrics differ from the stuff of your polyester duvet cover? The formula of a basic polyester might be $(CO.C_6H_4.CO.O.CH_2CH_2.O)_n$ – this is terylene, the original. The structure comprises this unit linked hundreds of times in long chains. These filaments are then twisted together into a yarn and woven into fabric in the traditional way. But nature's materials have hierarchically organized structures. Think of wood with its grain and cylindrical vessels. Spider silk, apparently a fine tough thread like nylon or terylene, isn't one substance at all, but a structured blend of at least two proteins that is orientated by its passage through the spider's spinnerets to produce its remarkable properties. Other materials, such as the shells of shellfish like abalone, are composites, with proteins and calcium carbonate interwoven. Engineered composite materials such as resin-bonded glass-fibre and carbon-fibre composites are gross in scale compared to abalone, and much less tough. The key is that between the molecular level and the scale visible to the human eye, biomaterials have intricate structures that create their special properties. Human-engineered materials lack this nanoscale organization.

Biomimeticians are now homing in on the nanoscale structures of composites such as abalone shell. They have realized that nature produces these structures with quite basic minerals such as calcium carbonate (invertebrate shells), calcium phosphate (vertebrate skeletons), and silica (radiolarians) by using organic templates to control the crystallization of the mineral. Sometimes, the organic template, its work done, drops away, leaving the mineral in its convolutions: the radiolarians of the ocean are an example; other times the mineral and organic tissue are interleaved, as in abalone shell, producing a composite material of exceptional strength.

Materials scientists are using templates of every imaginable kind. Even wood grain, for example, has been used in structuring zeolites, minerals with porous structures used in catalysis, separation, and adsorption. Living cells, bacterial parts, viruses such as the tobacco mosaic virus, and the phages that prey on bacteria have all been used as organic templates. Synthetic templates have been used as well: foams are obviously an attractive option, and structures similar to radiolarians have been made by mineralizing them.

Related to templating are the goals of self-assembly and inducing organic and electronic components to 'recognize' each other and interact. Human engineering has so far been top down – parts are brought together and assembled under the guiding eye of a person, aided by microscopes and micromanipulation techniques. But nature takes very small molecules and assembles them automatically, from the bottom up, by means of their natural affinities. Angela Belcher at the University of Texas in Austin (and about to move to MIT) has been using the structures of biological molecules such as polypeptides and even whole organisms, genetically engineered phages, to orientate nanoscale electromagnetic and optical substances for use in computing.

In a paper published in *Science* in May, Belcher and her colleagues reported producing liquid crystals of a complex of zinc sulphide and M13 bacteriophage. Liquid crystals (as used in the monitors of laptop computers and hand-held devices) have orientated crystal structures that can be induced by electrical signals to flip from one mode to another. Zinc sulphide is phosphorescent – it glows blue when irradiated by electrons – and is used in TV and desktop-computer screens. It is a normally an inert mineral material.

The technique works because, even outside living cells, proteins can recognize certain parts of other molecules and bind to them. In the course of evolution, proteins have not had to cope with man-made semiconductors but it has been possible to 'evolve' protein sequences that can recognize and bind to specific semiconductors and other electronic components. A gene for this 'recognition' protein sequence is inserted into the phage, which is then replicated by infecting its usual host bacterium. Finally, by choosing the right solvent and adding the zinc sulphide, the phage/zinc sulphide complex self-assembles into a centimetres-long transparent liquid crystal film that can be picked up with forceps. Embedded in it at regular intervals are nanodots of zinc sulphide only

3nm wide. Significant structure at the nano level has thus been achieved.

Such organic/inorganic hybrids could have many uses. The primary goal of Belcher's work is the quantum-dot computer element. The essence of a computer is something very small that can flip between two states – on and off. The ultimate prize, which has already been achieved as a one-off experiment, is an entity that can be flipped by a single electron: the quantum dot. Nanoscale liquid crystal arrays such as those devised by Belcher are potential quantum-dot devices.

Like Belcher's phages, many of nature's most ingenious machines can work outside the living cell. Engineers would like to replicate muscle tissue for use in robotics, and many forms of artificial muscle have been made using gels that contract and expand when stimulated electrically. But nature's own muscle material, using the proteins actin and myosin, will work outside the cell, and nature's ubiquitous energy source, the ATP motor, provides the power.

For years ATP (adenosine triphosphate) was called the powerhouse of the cell – it takes part in electron-transfer reactions that produce the energy for all cellular processes. But this was a metaphor; no one expected it actually to *rotate* like a turbine, yet this is in fact what it does. The ATP motor is an enzyme, ATP synthase, with a structure that has been likened to a mushroom: six pods sit around a spindle, and the reaction rotates around the six heads. In the cell the revolving reaction does not drive any rotational structure, the energy produced is passed down an electrochemical chain of reactions until it finds useful work to do, in moving a muscle for example. But Ricky Soong, George Bachand, Carlo Montemagno and their team at Cornell's Nanobiotechnology Center have succeeded in bridging the bio/engineering interface by attaching an inorganic rotor to the biological motor in an artificial environment and filming the motion, which runs at 1–8 revolutions per second.

One of nature's materials with fascinating engineering properties is DNA itself. DNA is literally a template, in that it reproduces itself by unpeeling its double helix, then adding bases to the single strands until two new double helices are formed. More than that: its helical nature means that it can transmit twisting motion into forward motion. This it does in bacteriophages where it is packed into the heads of the phages and discharged from them by such translational motion. DNA self-assembly is going to be increasingly used to orientate nanoscale materials.

Designers, engineers and inventors have, until recently, been imprisoned by the limits of human senses. We can copy only what we can see or know to be there. So, early examples of biomimcry like Catseyes and Velcro mimicked the visible phenomena of the cat's reflective layer in the eye and the clinging spines of the cocklebur. But with many natural phenomena *we couldn't see how they did it.* Two examples that made great biomimetic strides in 2002: the gecko's foot and spider silk. The gecko can climb smooth, vertical glass walls, and even climb upside down on the ceiling, with feet so finely divided that their structure was a mystery until recently. Engineers have known for some time that the ability of a spider's web to catch a fly and hold it without rebounding is the equivalent in our world of a net that could catch a plane in mid flight. How do such creatures do it?

What the gecko's foot and spider's silk have in common is significant structural organization on a scale far finer than anything achieved by conventional engineering. A team under Dr Kellar Autumn at Lewis and Clark College, Portland, Oregon, and Professor Robert Full at Berkeley have established that the gecko mechanism is dry, and that it does not involve suction, capillary action or anything else the lay person might imagine. Each foot has almost half a million bristles, or setae, and each bristle ramifies into hundreds of finer, spatula-shaped projections. The gecko pushes the spatula-shaped projections forward a little on the surface, after which any downward pull is resisted very strongly. Molecular forces that come into play at the very small dimensions of the bristles are responsible for the adhesion. Geckos have a special toe curling/uncurling routine that enables them to stick or unpeel at will.

Get a grip by learning how a gecko clings to glass.

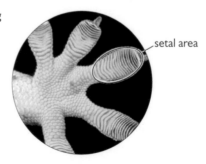

setal area

A product using something like the gecko principle is already on the market: a fabric trademarked as Greptile from 3M. Greptile allows a solid grip on virtually any surface, using miniature, ultra-precise and three-dimensional surface structures. Greptile is used for sports equipment, clothes, shoes, and accessories such as gloves and shoulder straps. It is of course reminiscent of Velcro and represents a kind of Velcro for the age of nanotechnology: the hooks and eyes of Velcro being large-scale; Greptile nanoscale.

Spider silk, produced in industrial quantities, has long been regarded as a great prize. In June, a team at Nexia Biotechnologies in Quebec, working to a US Army contract, announced that they had implanted spider-silk genes in goats. The silk-proteins were then spun using various techniques to produce a fibre with some of the properties of natural spider silk. At present the extensibility is far too great and the tenacity – the resistance to tearing once one has started – is well down on the original. The key to the ultimate properties of spider silk are the chemical and physical reactions that occur in the spinnerets and these will have to be mimicked as well to match natural spider silk.

It will be some time before spider silk reaches the market but Lotus Effect paint is already there and thriving. The great Sacred Lotus (*Nelumbo nucifera*) is a plant whose leaves repel dirt – even glue rolls off them without adhering. And although the mechanism by which it does this has only recently been discovered, the plant has been revered for millennia as a symbol of purity. It is sacred to Hinduism and to several other Asian religions, especially Buddhism. The microstructure of the leaves that allows this phenomenon to occur was observed in the course of an exhaustive electron micrographic study of plant structures by Wilhelm Barthlott, a biologist at the University of Bonn – the kind of fundamental research that to the layperson seems hopelessly obscure. But Barthlott discovered that the microsurface of the leaf – waxy, water-repellent bobbles like the uncut pile of a carpet – ensures that water never gets further than sitting on top of the bobbles, wetting any dirt with which it comes into contact.

The first application, an exterior silicone coating for houses, Lotusan, was introduced by ISPO Gmbh in March 1999. As of October 2002, in Germany alone some 30 million square metres of facades have been successfully coated with the paint. Ironically, the hero of the saga, the Sacred Lotus itself, is a species under threat in India from human pollution and enviromental change. The lesson here does not need to be underlined.

Biomimetics doesn't have to be seen as slavishly mimicking some creature. Activ glass, a self-cleaning glass developed by Pilkington, is based not on any creature or specific natural mechanism but on the idea of self-cleaning. Activ glass uses a very fine layer of two coatings – one hydrophilic and the other photocatalytic – to enable rainwater to keep the glass clean. Intriguingly, Activ glass is almost a mirror image of Lotus Effect paint: Lotus Effect coatings are bumpy and hydrophobic, Activ glass smooth and hydrophilic. The glass works by preventing droplet formation: rain 'sheets' on the surface and carries away any dirt. The photocatalytic layer is needed to oxidize organic matter such as bird droppings which otherwise would be impervious to the rainwater.

Activ glass and Lotus Effect paint are two examples of the burgeoning trend towards 'smart' building materials. The phrase 'smart buildings' conjures an image in most minds of a wired-up, computer-controlled house in which all the services can be activated by computer or a remote control, but this other kind of smartness – eliminating maintenance in the materials themselves – seems likely to be just as important. There is an almost Zen-like satisfaction to be gained from the idea of making our buildings incorruptible by the usual agents of decay.

Biomimetics is not only about nanoscale effects. Some of the most intriguing ideas involve large-scale structures that turn out to have more in common than you'd expect. What, for example, has a solar panel array in a space satellite got to do with negotiating the Tokyo subway and the way that leaves unfurl from the bud? The unlikely answer is origami – the Japanese art of paper folding. Leaves and solar cells have the same basic function, to soak up as much sunlight as possible, and to do this they need the maximum surface area. But while leaves are in the bud and a satellite is being launched, solar panels and leaves alike have to pack down as tightly as possible. The Miura-Ori folding technique (a form of origami), developed in Japan by Koryo Miura over the last thirty years for solar-cell arrays and also as a folding technology for one-pull street maps, now emerges in work from Professor Julian Vincent's team (originally at Reading University, now at the Centre for Biomimetics and Natural Technologies, in the Department of Mechanical Engineering at the University of Bath) as the method by which beech and hornbeam leaves unfurl – a piece of reverse biomimesis, if you like.

Out in the world of beech and hornbeam trees we encounter camouflage, one of nature's neatest tricks and one long attractive to biomimeticians. To be well camouflaged is the life-or-death strategy of many creatures, so it is not surprising that in the life-or-death situation of war, engineers should have turned to nature for ideas. The familiar earth-pattern painted camouflage was first applied in World War I but Alex Parfitt, working with Julian Vincent at Bath University, is developing a biomimetic camouflage based on the colour- and pattern-generating systems of cephalopods such as squid, octopus and cuttlefish. These creatures can change their colour to blend in with their surroundings, and many flat fish such as plaice and flounder can do likewise. The sophistication of this is such that, placed on an artificial background such as a black and white chequerboard, a plaice or flounder can imitate the pattern.

The cephalopods have three kinds of colour organs: chromatophores, iridophores and leucophores. The chromatophores are pigmented organs that come in three colours – red, yellow and brown/black and you can think of them like the colours of process printing. The leucophores reflect light at the same wavelength as the current ambient light and the iridophores reflect iridescent colour. The chromatophores contain radial muscles and they sit on top of the iridophores and leucophores. When the chromatophores expand, displaying their colours, they blot out the iridophores and leucophores, and when they are contracted they allow the cells to reflect to the maximum degree. Not all of this complex system is mimicked in the bio-camouflage. The colour changes occur in a gel that can respond by reflecting ambient light rather like the iridophores. A certain amount of sensing and electronics is necessary but the aim is to be as naturally responsive as possible.

The Bath group's work is funded by the Defence Logistics Organisation (DLO) and Engineering and Physical Sciences Research Council (EPSRC) and, because it is a defence project, how much detail is going to be revealed is uncertain. The camouflage will be deployed by another biomimetic technique: Julian Vincent's beech-leaf unfolding technique, already mentioned.

There is something inherently playful about biomimetics. Lateral thinking is the order of the day, a taste for visual puns helps, and the natural quiddities of the creatures involved add spice to the work. Picasso would have liked biomimetics. When he saw camouflage in

World War I he exclaimed, 'Yes it is we who made it, that is cubism.'
He made many sculptures in the 1950s in which natural and man-made forms were punned. See, for example, his *Baboon and Young* (1951), the head of which was made from two American toy cars. And the designer of Volkswagen's New Beetle had a little of Picasso's spirit when he made the rear of the car almost identical to the front.

In biomimetics, the line between work and play can be elastic. Julian Vincent tells of the time he was working on viscoelastic extensible cuticle from the abdomen of the locust. The lab joke was that it would surely one day produce a commercial product to be called Visconix, the perfect all-purpose body stocking. This notion was written up straight-faced in *New Scientist* and took on a life of its own. Garment manufacturers were knocking on the door, promising grants for this wonder material. A big US firm wanted to produce nappy liners and already had a slogan 'leaves no red line' – before the difficulties of working with locust cuticle finally defeated the idea.

A serious idea that at first seems as wacky as Visconix is the Ro-Ro gripper. Loosely based on an elephant's trunk, this is a soft toroidal structure that can, attached to a robot arm, pick up delicate objects of any shape without damage, by using a rolling action to completely envelop them. Invented by freelance designer Adrian Marshall, of Crafty Tech Ltd, the Ro-Ro is a classic of large-scale biomimesis. Marshall is very much a designer in the Picasso-playful mode: he makes robots, such as the frog jumper and Cyber Snail, seen on BBC TV's *Technogames*, and also the more serious Marshalling Yard (pun intended), an ingenious method of bringing objects on production belts into neat rows by the use of speed waves. This is the surfing principle in nature: objects dropped at random into breaking waves fetch up on the beach on the crest of the waves. Marshall is interested in the way things move rather than their composition and his work is a reminder that biomimetics isn't just a matter of nanoscale materials science, but also of lateral thinking and Picassoesque inventiveness.

Global warming: where are the snows of yesteryear?

TIM RADFORD

The snows of Kilimanjaro are disappearing fast.
But that's not all.

There has been an ice cap on the summit of Mt Kilimanjaro, in Tanzania, for 11,700 years, according to Lonnie Thompson and a team from Ohio State University, who have been exhuming the evidence of past climates from corings drilled through the annual layers of snow. They reported in *Science* on 17 October 2002 that they found signals of catastrophic droughts that plagued the tropics 8300 years ago, 5200 years ago and 4000 years ago. The last drought, which lasted three hundred years, could have been the one that, according to historical records, rocked the Egyptian empire and turned yet more of the Sahara into barren wilderness. Around 9500 years ago, Africa would have been much wetter: Lake Chad, now 17,000 square kilometres, would have covered twenty times that area, and been larger than the modern Caspian Sea.

But the team also brought back more urgent data. They calculated that the mountain's ice cap had lowered by seventeen metres since 1962, and retreated two metres since 2000. A University of Massachusetts team studied aerial photographs and other records and noted that between 1912 and 2000 the surface area of Kilimanjaro's ice cap had shrunk by 80 per cent. Since ice has been coming and going without human help on the summit of Kilimanjaro for ten thousand years, nobody wanted to make the link directly to human-induced global warming. But Dr Thompson warned that the ice fields of Kilimanjaro could disappear within fifteen years.

'Whatever happened to cause these dramatic climate changes in the past, could certainly occur again,' he said. 'But today, 70 per cent of the world's population lives in the tropics. They would be dramatically affected by events of this magnitude. We have to find out what causes them to happen.'

Kilimanjaro may be a special case, but it is not the only abode of the vanishing snows. Lakes have been growing, rapidly, on a number of glacier surfaces. Ice reflects sunlight. Water absorbs and transmits it, triggering a feedback that leads to more melting. One global research project confirmed that the Gangotri glacier in the Indian Himalayas is retreating at an ever-faster rate: meltwater from this glacier feeds the Ganges river basin, upon which hundreds of millions depend. 'Glaciers in most areas of the world are known to be receding. But glaciers in the Himalaya are wasting at alarming and accelerating rates,' Jeff Kargel, of the US Geological Survey, warned at a meeting of the American Geophysical Union in May.

A team from the NASA Goddard Space Flight Center in Maryland reported in June that the flow from the Greenland ice sheet has been accelerating during recent summers. In winter, the ice moved at an average of 31.3cm per day; in summer it speeded up to 40cm. A second study from the University of Colorado showed that melting of the Greenland ice sheet surface had increased by 20 per cent in the last twenty years, in line with an increase in summer temperatures of 0.25°C. A team from the University of Fairbanks, Alaska, calculated that Alaskan glaciers had contributed to 9 per cent of the global rise in sea level this century. Aerial studies confirmed that around 85 per cent of the glaciers they had been watching had lost vast portions of their mass in the last fifty years.

The year 1998 was the warmest since records began. It was, notoriously, also the year of the longest and fiercest El Niño, a natural Pacific disturbance that periodically seems to delay the monsoons of India, and brings floods and storms to normally arid parts of the American Pacific coast. El Niño in fact began in 1997, and was signalled by calamitous forest fires in Indonesia. Rainforests are not famous for being combustible, but the tropical moist forests of the archipelago have been heavily and illegally logged, making it easier for fire to take hold not just in the canopy but in huge tropical peat swamps, some of them twelve metres deep. The fire created a noxious cloud of yellow haze that for several months covered an area of 15 million square kilometres. This cloud closed airports, disrupted trade, shut down schools, had a serious impact on respiratory health and cost regional economies an estimated $2 billion.

Where are the snows of yesteryear? The retreating ice of Mount Kilimanjaro, Tanzania.

It also fuelled global warming: Susan Page of Leicester University and colleagues reported in *Nature* on 7 November 2002 that the peat fires pumped up to 2.6 billion tonnes of carbon into the atmosphere as carbon dioxide. This is anything up to 40 per cent of the annual global production of atmospheric carbon dioxide by burning oil, coal and gas, and according to *Nature* is roughly equal to all the carbon dioxide that is normally absorbed by vegetation and algae, from the atmosphere, in the course of a normal year. Page had begun work in the region several years before the event, and was there during the fires.

'Ours is not a desk job,' she said. 'We were there. We breathed it in. It could be a thousand years or more of peat accumulation that went in a few months.' She warned that fires were also burning in the same area during 2002, a year marked by catastrophic floods in Europe, a drought in India and the start of another, but somewhat weaker, El Niño. By late October, climate scientists had enough evidence to go on: 2002 was a year for the record books – it was the second-hottest year ever recorded. Scientists confirmed that eight of the ten warmest years since records began have been since 1994. For those with rusty arithmetic, there have been only eight years since 1994.

Cloning: a show called Cats

TIM RADFORD

Cc owes her life to a millionaire's pet project.

They called her Cc, which might stand for Copy cat, Carbon copy
or even Calico cat, which is what she was: a tiny orange, black and brown
kitten, born to a surrogate mother tabby called Allie, and cloned from
a cell taken from a parent-twin called Rainbow. And although Texas
A&M University has in the past cloned piglets, a Boer goat, an Angus bull
and a Brahma bull to add to the world's pool of cloned sheep, mice and
so on, Cc has a distinction: she is the world's first cloned pet. She is fruit
of the Missyplicity project, funded by a multimillionaire to investigate
the possibility of cloning a pet dog called Missy.

Cc's birth notice appeared formally in *Nature* on 21 February 2002.
In fact, the world first heard of her on 14 February, when a US newspaper
– in the words of one commentator – 'let the cat out of the bag'. Cc was
the only survivor from multiple attempts: in all, 87 cloned embryos were
created, and transferred into eight recipients. The team ended up with

Cc: the ultimate in pet projects.

one failed pregnancy and one live clone. Her human begetters announced that DNA analysis confirmed that the kitten was indeed a clone, or genetic copy, even though her coat colouring followed a slightly different pattern. 'The pattern of pigmentation in multicoloured animals is the result of genetic factors as well as developmental factors that are not controlled by genotype,' said Mark Westhusin of the university's College of Veterinary Medicine. 'With each new species cloned, we learn more about how this technology might be applied to improving the health of animals and humans.'

Animal welfare groups expressed concern. Cat fanciers suggested that a clone could not be registered as a pedigreed cat, because cloning would sidestep all the genetic rules of breeding. But Arthur Caplan, director of the centre for bioethics at the University of Pennsylvania school of medicine told MSNBC.com: 'The future of cloning is in animals, not people. When people understand what cloning is, they understand that you can't be immortal. Cloning doesn't copy a person... It only becomes of interest to the desperate and the very, very self-absorbed. But for animals, including pets, cloning has a very lucrative future, and business and researchers know this.'

He added: 'We love each other, at least on good days, for our minds and they can't be copied. But we love our pets for their bodies, and they can be copied.' A US firm called Genetic Savings and Clone stores tissue for potential pet clones. Its chief executive told the journal *Science* that his business existed because of public demand. 'When we launched two years ago, we got thousands of calls within the first 24 hours.'

Supersymmetry:
too beautiful to be wrong?

GRAHAM FARMELO

String, squarks, sparticles and the answer to everything
(maybe).

It was beauty that made Einstein famous. Not his rugged good looks,
but the gorgeousness of his 1915 General Theory of Relativity. Contrary
to popular myth, this theory did not suddenly eclipse Newton's by
convincingly accounting for new experimental data on the bending
of starlight. Rather, it was the beauty of Einstein's theory that persuaded
a handful of influential colleagues of its fundamental truth. It was to
be another 35 years before experimenters demonstrated convincingly
that the beautiful theory could hack it not only in the minds of theorists
but in the laboratory of the universe.

Physicists are now enjoying something resembling of a rerun of
this story, with the extended drama of supersymmetry, still unresolved

after almost three decades. Formulated by several groups of European theorists in the mid 1970s, the supersymmetry theory of fundamental particles rapidly gained wide approval among theoreticians. It was simply too beautiful to be wrong. The theory makes plenty of unique predictions but, at the end of 2002, not one of them has been confirmed, despite huge efforts from experimenters. Although the overwhelming majority of theorists are keeping faith with the theory, a few have lost patience. Martin Veltman, the Dutch Nobel-garlanded theoretician, is a champion of the supersymmetric malcontents. In seminars, he growls that he is tired of hearing that 'there's only one more corner to turn, only to hear that there's another corner'. So is it time to junk supersymmetry?

Just as Einstein's general theory had to contend with the practically faultless performance of Newton's theory of gravity, supersymmetry has its own cross to bear – it purports to supersede a theory that has generated not a single embarrassing conflict with experiment. This theory, dubbed unprepossessingly as the Standard Model, is based on the trusted foundations of quantum theory and the special theory of relativity and describes the electromagnetic, weak and strong interactions between the handful of fundamental particles (gravity is beyond its scope). It turns out that the universe consists of what might be called 'bricks' and 'mortar' – the 'bricks' are the family of six leptons (including the familiar electron) together with another family of six quarks (including the up and down quarks which exist inside every proton and neutron in the atomic nucleus). The interactions between the 'bricks' are mediated by the 'mortar' – a set of particles that includes the photon, familiar as the particle of light.

We can think of all these point-like particles as spinning, a bit like a sub-microscopic, point-like Earth whirling around its axis. In nature, particles can be classed into those that have a spin measured in whole numbers (0, 1, 2 etc), and those that have spins that are multiples of a half ($\frac{1}{2}$, $\frac{3}{2}$, $\frac{5}{2}$ etc). Every 'brick' particle has spin $\frac{1}{2}$, whereas every 'mortar' particle has spin 1.

Although the Standard Model has a perfectly clean bill of health from the experimenters' point of view, the theoreticians are profoundly unhappy with their creation. Among its most embarrassing shortcomings are its failure to explain the masses of the 'bricks', its unexplained 'free parameters' and the fact that it makes no sense at all if it is applied to particles at ultra-energies. And there is a clear and rather unsatisfying disparity between the way the Model treats the spin ½ 'bricks' and the spin 1 'mortar'. Why are they so different?

Enter on a white stallion the theory of supersymmetry, an ingeniously elaborated version of the Standard Model, replete with beautiful symmetries. In supersymmetry, the equations of the theory remain the same if the symbols representing spin ½ particles are swapped with ones representing spin 1 particles. In this theory, the successful framework of the Standard Model remains perfectly intact – just as Einstein's General Theory of Relativity could reproduce the successes of its Newtonian predecessor. But the new symmetries bring with them a host of new insights and predictions.

For one thing, supersymmetry leads us to rethink the very nature of space and time. In everyday life, we measure these concepts using numbers: 'She walked 50m along the road at 6 o'clock.' Einstein based his relativity theory on just these ideas. But if supersymmetry is correct, space and time are not fundamentally measurable by ordinary numbers but in terms of quantum dimensions. Pleasingly for the manufacturers of clocks and rulers, these quantum dimensions would not impinge on measurements made day to day – unless, just possibly, you happen to be one of the few thousand particle physicists studying matter under the most extreme conditions that humans can contrive on Earth.

Most strikingly for the physicists who worked on supersymmetry, the theory provided a natural framework for unifying all the fundamental interactions, including gravity (which, remember, was not part of the Standard Model). Indeed, supersymmetry *demands* that the gravitational force exists in addition to the other fundamental interactions – if Einstein had not discovered the General Theory of Relativity, then the formulation of supersymmetry alone would have led to its discovery sixty years later.

According to supersymmetry, every particle with half-integer spin (eg spin ½) has a counterpart in the other category, with a whole-number spin. Each of these counterparts is known as a sparticle. So for example, electrons and quarks (all with spin ½) have corresponding spinless sparticles known respectively as selectrons and squarks. No wonder the patois of supersymmetry enthusiasts has been dubbed 'slanguage'.

It could be that this theory of matter at its finest level will solve a problem at the opposite end of the distance scale, concerning the contents of the entire universe. For decades, cosmologists have been unable to account for about 90 per cent of the matter in the universe –

Products of the atom-smasher: the conditions are similar to those
in the first trillionth of a second of time.

that's about ten thousand trillion trillion trillion (10^{40}) tonnes of it.
As Lady Bracknell might have remarked, to have mislaid a little of the
universe may be regarded as unfortunate, to have lost most of it looks like
carelessness. Could it be that the unobserved matter consists of sparticles?
This is currently one of the most promising candidates for understanding
why so much matter in the universe seems to have gone AWOL.

Supersymmetry has many other virtues. It enables the otherwise
inexplicable pattern among the masses of the fundamental 'bricks' to
be understood at a stroke. And, amid the hieroglyphics of the theory,
the underlying symmetries make it possible to remove the difficulties
that thwart the Standard Model's ability to calculate how some of its
particles behave at ultra-high energies on the scale they encountered
during their brief lives at the beginning of the universe, during the
Big Bang.

Could nature be so perverse as to fail to be described by such a theory?
The reason we don't yet know the answer to that question is that
experimenters have not yet managed to ask the right questions of nature
to be given the definitive answer. Plans are, however, well under way for

experiments that will enable us to see once and for all whether nature is fundamentally supersymmetric.

Most promising is the atom-smasher (known to insiders as the LHC) now being built in Geneva at CERN, the European laboratory for particle physics. This machine will allow experimenters routinely to create conditions of extremely high energy and high density, similar to the ones only a trillionth (10^{-12}) of a second after the beginning of time, in the Big Bang. In this torrid environment, the most energy-dense ever to be created on the planet, the sparticles should emerge, weighing between 500 and 2000 times as much as the proton. Also destined to make its inaugural appearance is the Higgs particle, believed to be partly responsible for most of the fundamental particles having mass. Supersymmetric theorists believe that the Higgs particle, the one particle of the Standard Model that has eluded us, should be no more than 130 times as heavy as the proton.

Leading CERN theorist and supersymmetry enthusiast John Ellis hopes to see data confirming supersymmetry pouring out of the detectors at the new LHC machine within a month of its opening in 2007. 'If we do not see a sparticle and a Higgs particle with the LHC, then I'll be prepared to admit that the theory must be wrong.'

It is just possible, however, that physicists over in Chicago will beat the CERN experimenters to it. Over at the Fermi National Accelerator Laboratory in Batavia, near Chicago, they are currently preparing their own powerful accelerator to collide protons with antiprotons, hoping to discover sparticles and Higgs particles among the debris of the collisions.

In 2003, it is also possible that accelerators at Stanford in California and at Tsukuba in Japan will also uncover tell-tale signs that the Standard Model is wanting and needs supersymmetric enhancements. These accelerators are now in a hectic race to produce and study vast quantities of subatomic particles containing at least one heavy quark known as the b quark (b stands for 'bottom' or 'beauty') or its corresponding antiquark. Particles that contain one or two b quarks or antiquarks are known in the trade as 'naked bottoms'. At the moment, the decays of these particles are described to wonderful accuracy by the Standard Model, but supersymmetry does predict that there should be some tell-tale departures from the Model's predictions. So it could be that close studies of naked bottoms in Japan or the US will be the first clear experimental heraldings of the need for supersymmetry. Perhaps 2003 will be the year this elusive symmetry comes out of the wings and appears centre stage?

While the experimenters have been tooling up, theoreticians have moved energetically ahead and formulated string theory and its closely related successor, M-theory. Both are based on supersymmetry and therefore assume it to be correct. These theorists believe that everything fundamentally consists of tiny pieces of string, each about a millionth of a billionth of a billionth of a billionth of a centimetre long. In this picture, electrons and quarks and the force-mediating particles are not actually particles at all, but are each a vibrating piece of string, much too small to see. Again, it is the alluring beauty of the theory that encourages theorists to believe firmly that they are on the right track.

String theory is now by far the most promising area in theoretical research into the fundamental nature of matter. One of the most interesting avenues has stemmed from the work of the late British physicist Paul Dirac, who predicted the existence of antimatter on the basis of his beautiful theory of the electron, a year before experimenters first detected a single *anti*-electron in the cosmic rays raining down from the summer skies of California. Antimatter has subsequently proved painfully difficult to produce on Earth but, as if to celebrate the centenary of Dirac's birth in 1902, physicists at CERN wrote in the 3 October edition of *Nature* in 2002 that they had produced the first-ever batch of antimatter, in the form of 50,000 anti-hydrogen atoms (in particle physics, that counts as a shed-load).

Dirac, the patron saint of aestheticism in theoretical physics, was fascinated by Einstein's General Theory of Relativity – a geometric theory of gravity – which he regarded as the exemplar of a mathematical theory whose beauty was a more powerful commendation than mere agreement with experiment. He once explained the appeal of mathematical beauty by comparing the formulation of the equations of fundamental physics using the nearest thing he ever came to an accessible analogy: 'It's a question of finding things fit together well. You're solving a problem, it might be a crossword puzzle, and things don't fit, and you conclude you've made some mistakes. Suddenly you think of corrections and everything fits.'

In 1963, Dirac produced a special version of Einstein's theory, featuring a negatively curved, saddle-shaped space called 'anti de Sitter' space, after the Dutch mathematician Willem de Sitter (1872–1934). In this space, the sum of the angles of a triangle is less than 180 degrees, which is the total in ordinary flat space. Thanks to the 32-year-old Argentine superstar Juan Maldacena, at the Institute of Advanced Study in Princeton, this work is now the hottest topic in M-theory. According to Maldacena, our universe may be a three-dimensional membrane living in a four-dimensional anti de Sitter space. 'This picture is looking increasingly plausible,' says British M-theory expert Michael Duff, of the University of Michigan. 'If it is correct, then the universe is like the wall of Plato's cave and we are the shadows projected on it.'

These are heady times for M-theorists. They can enjoy the luxury of creating truly beautiful theories, attending to the fundamental principles of physics and observing the laws of logic – but without the oppressive constraints of awkward experimental results to cramp their style. Yet could it be that nature has a surprise in store? Will one ugly fact destroy the entire supersymmetrical edifice, bringing down M-theory with it? Or is nature finally going to give its imprimatur to these beautiful theories, as Einstein and Dirac believed it could be trusted to do? To paraphrase Lady Bracknell's creator, beauty will out.

The Johannesburg summit and down to earth in Alex

BEN WISNER

How world agreements could help the poor or fill the pockets of the rich.

Until Johannesburg's World Summit on Sustainable Development, in 2002, only residents and historians of the anti-apartheid struggle knew Alexandra Township. 'Alex' is now well known as the other pole of economic development and human well-being, frequently referred to by foreign journalists in juxtaposition to the high-class enclave of Stanton, two miles away, where the summit was held.

I conducted research in Alexandra Township between 1995 and 1997. I came with the intention of working on the problem of flash flooding that affects this area. Three small streams once flowed down the slope from Louis Botha Avenue to the Jukskei River. These small streams were long ago covered over. Shacks were built over them.

Underground drains are supposed to carry run-off down to the river, but they are blocked by refuse. In the north-east corner of Alexandra, near the cemetery, the Jukskei River cuts into ten-metre-high cliffs made of compacted garbage. Here shacks built by former Mozambican war refugees, and other marginal people, fall regularly into the river. The statistically calculable fifty-year flood could destroy 900 shacks and endanger between 4400 and 10,500 people.

I thought people would have flood risk high on their mental agendas. However, so hard is life in Alexandra, and so numerous the risks, that in focus-group discussions flood was never ranked higher than seventh. More commonly, people mentioned water supply and sanitation; the danger to their children from the speeding minibuses that serve as public transportation; shack fires; violence; and bad air quality from the thousands of metal drums filled with burning mineral coal used for cooking and for heat in the winter. It can get so cold in winter that the Alexandra Clinic, a non-governmental, non-profit health facility, directs newborns and their mothers to a network of volunteer 'warm houses' in the neighbourhood.

Many people still have to use a bucket latrine system, and the resulting accumulation is collected by the city irregularly. Over the years courtyards have been subdivided, so that renters crowd every available corner, where they live in shelters made of scrap wood, corrugated aluminium, and even cardboard and plastic.

Since my work in Alexandra the newly elected authorities in Johannesburg have forcefully evicted hundreds of families. I suppose if one is not concerned where the expelled families end up, this is a victory for flood-risk reduction. One local headline read, 'Moving Alexandra Squatters Good for Environment'. These evictions have been accompanied by plans to make Nelson Mandela's former house in Alexandra into a national monument, along with some tree planting, establishment of a 'state of the art information resource centre', and a good deal of paid work by urban redevelopment consultants.

On the Sunday before the official close of the Johannesburg summit, forty thousand people marched from Alexandra to the summit venue. They wanted to remind delegates of the needs and demands of real people in South Africa and all around the world. What had been going on in South Africa and many other countries before, during, and after all of

Flooding

Natural catastrophes could have caused up to $70 billion worth of damage worldwide by the close of 2002, according to UN climate change experts. By October, insurers had counted 526 major natural disasters, killing 9400, making hundreds of thousands homeless, affecting millions.

More than 40 per cent of deaths and 66 per cent of economic losses were due to floods. The worst floods in Europe for 150 years may have caused insured losses of $2–5 billion.

Floods and landslides in Indonesia destroyed 100,000 homes. Floods in China killed 500 and destroyed 600,000 homes; the economic cost was put at more than $3 billion.

Meanwhile, the worst drought in a century affected 800,000 people in north and eastern China.

the speeches and commitments to poverty alleviation – besides evictions in the name of cleaning up the environment – was massive privatization of electricity and water supplies. In South Africa, twenty thousand families each month were being cut off from the supply of electricity due to privatization of services and the resulting increase in price. Electricians were also being made redundant as the public utility fell into private hands. The Soweto Electricity Crisis Committee was formed to put unemployed electricians in touch with the poor, who were thus illegally reconnected. That struggle continued while the summit went on, and continues still. The Soweto Electricity Crisis Committee and many other similar citizen initiatives were among the marchers from Alexandra to the Summit venue.

Viewed against this backdrop, one should ask what difference the final declaration and programme of action coming out of the World Conference on Sustainable Development might make to the people who live in Alexandra Township, and to the poor elsewhere in South Africa and the world.

Besides direct benefits to health and incomes, can the summit make any difference to disaster vulnerability? Will it? These are two separate questions. The potential is very great. For the first time a major international meeting focused on the interconnections between wealth, poverty, governance, the natural world and a variety of risks. These connections have seldom been highlighted despite decades of activity. Even the International Decade for Natural Disaster Reduction (IDNDR) didn't do this. It dealt mostly with technical questions, linking earth and atmospheric science with planning and policy. People's access to basic services such as water and electricity were never addressed. During the last three years of the IDNDR, when attention was turned to reducing earthquake risk in cities, the form and quality of municipal government in a participating city was accepted at face value and never questioned; it never became part of the research.

Water, sanitation, and renewable energy came up at Johannesburg in a more holistic way than they did during the International Water Supply and Sanitation Decade (1980–89) or the World Conference on Energy, held in Nairobi in 1980. Targets were defined. By 2015 the number of people without access to safe water is to be cut in half. This is specific and concrete. It would mean that 880 million people would have improved access to water by 2015. Childhood diarrhoea would decrease; this is the number-one killer of children under five in the world today, claiming 6000 young lives each day. Blindness from fly-borne trachoma would decrease; this infection is easily prevented by washing the face and hands, and is responsible for 6 million cases of blindness in the world today and 146 million active cases that could result in blindness. In addition, healthier people can produce more, and families can save on health expenditures if their members are not sick from water-related diseases. Thus it is safe to predict that incomes would go up.

Targets for use of renewable energy are less specific and more modest, yet the spirit of the Johannesburg meeting was to acknowledge that clean, cheap, accessible energy for all is an important part of achieving sustainable development. Instead of the 10 per cent or even 15 per cent increase worldwide in energy from renewable sources that many delegates wanted, the summit only agreed on a 'substantial increase' with 'a sense of urgency'. The word 'urgency' seems mild when one considers that 2 billion people do not have access to reliable, clean forms of energy, including nine out of ten Africans. If implemented, the commitment to renewable energy would mean that in Alexandra the pall of coal smoke in the winter would disappear and illness from air pollution would decrease. The health costs of cooking with wood and coal and dung as fuel are enormous in many lands. For example, 800,000 people a year are thought to die from smoke-related respiratory disease each year in India, and some 2 million people worldwide.

So the Johannesburg commitment to improved access to water and renewable energy could bring great benefits. But before the cheering starts, one has to remember that at the moment thousands of people are being cut off from electricity supplies in South Africa, and that in the wake of privatization of water supplies in many countries the price has risen beyond the ability of the poor to pay. In South Africa, Ghana, Bolivia, Colombia, and El Salvador people are protesting the privatization of water as I write. Therefore the great potential benefits of these two Johannesburg agreements will only be achieved if they are implemented in certain ways and not others.

Firstly, implementation of new water supply and renewable energy projects in slums and villages would have to be done in a participatory fashion. Such ambitious infrastructure construction would be unfeasible, unsustainable and possibly dangerous if conducted from the top down, utilizing contractors and private firms. It would be unfeasible because it would simply cost too much. It would be unsustainable because without the benefit of local knowledge, such schemes would be hard to design and would be costly to maintain without local involvement. The danger comes from the creeping privatization of public utilities. International corporations are running public water supplies in many countries. The cost to the consumer nearly always goes up with privatization of water and electricity – one of the things being protested by the 40,000 people who marched from Alexandra to the site of the Johannesburg Summit.

So, assuming citizens would be involved in a variety of ways in such new water and energy schemes, the spin-offs for increased local networking and self-organization could be great. Increased self-organization in squatter settlements and remote villages alike is a main prerequisite of disaster risk reduction. People better organized can more easily become better prepared, better able to respond to hazard warnings, better able to demand attention to hazards by government.

Secondly, there are also some very specific technical links between a variety of common natural hazards and improvements in access to water and to clean energy. In the course of most local, small-scale water projects, an opportunity arises for residents to study and to become more aware of the local relief and pattern of water flow in the watershed where they live. Early warning of flash flooding could easily be built into this phase of a water project. For example, in Honduras and Jamaica, women in the highlands have been trained to monitor stream flow and report increases that could herald flooding in a few hours or days. Measures to mitigate drought could also be piggybacked on the construction of a village drinking-water supply. With the availability of rural electricity provided by solar, wind or microhydro technologies, a further foundation is provided for more widespread and reliable communication systems that could be used for transmitting a warning message. Use of renewable energy for domestic purposes, such as cooking, would prevent the cutting of trees that anchor slopes, and reduce the risk of landslides and flooding.

In both the case of water-supply improvements, and substitution of alternatives for wood fuel in the kitchen, great health benefits can be expected – reduction in diarrhoea for one, and reduction in respiratory disease from woodsmoke for another. In turn, savings to the household from not having to travel as often to the health post and buy medicine may go to further improvements in nutrition and well-being. A healthier labour force will work harder and perhaps more productively, since water and electricity could provide the basis for new rural and home-based industries. Natural hazards research has shown repeatedly that it is not only better-organized localities that have the capacity to resist extreme events, and the resilience to recover quickly, but localities composed of well-nourished and healthy individuals, and households with diverse and productive livelihoods.

The Johannesburg summit failed to endorse the Kyoto treaty on climate change. Gains in security for the most vulnerable people in the world due to successful small-scale water and energy projects could easily be wiped out by increased climate instability. This could work in several ways. First, the frequency and severity of extreme events, both floods and droughts, is likely to increase. There is evidence that this is already happening. Secondly, many of the poor will continue to be plagued and weakened by epidemics of dengue fever, malaria, and other insect-borne diseases that accompany El Niño events. Thirdly, development assistance finance could be diverted by rich countries if they have to spend hundred of billions on their own coastal defences against sea-level rises and flooding. Yet again at Johannesburg the magic figure of 0.7 per cent of GNP to be budgeted as development aid by rich countries was tabled. This suggested target has been around for thirty years, and has never been attained.

There were also no new agreements about farm subsidies. Rich countries pay their farmers hundreds of billions of dollars and euros in subsidies each year. This effectively blocks imports of agricultural goods from the poor South. A reorganization of the world's trading system that levels the playing field for a multitude of small farmers could revolutionize livelihoods, and thus bring about greater capacity to resist extreme natural events and resilience to recover from them. Without such an overhaul of the global economy, investments in water supply and renewable energy can make only small, marginal improvements in welfare.

There are schemes afoot to offer some of the people crowded into Alexandra Township housing sites on land on the other side of the Jukskei River. There are also plans to clean up the river, bringing down its astronomical coliform bacteria count. If plans for Alexandra are implemented, there could be more and better schools, a modern shopping precinct, and more recreational land. In microcosm, the tension between plan and implementation can be seen in 'Alex', the one historic 'black spot' that apartheid was never able to eliminate from near the heart of its financial and industrial capital. Alexandra Township could become a vital cultural, residential and commercial centre in its own right. It all depends on *how* such plans are implemented. Evictions, confrontations and utility cut-offs are not the way. So, too, the way in which the Johannesburg targets for water and renewable energy come to be implemented will determine their long-term consequences, and these, in turn, will influence how many newborn babies leave the Alexandra Clinic headed for a chilly and unsanitary home on a winter's day or towards a warm, healthy and safe one.

Malaria: the secrets of a killer

NEIL HALL

The unravelling of the genetic machinery of malaria
and the mosquito that carries it.

In terms of shortening life expectancy, malaria is out on its own.
Its victims are almost all under the age of five and it kills one child
every forty seconds. In western society we may never encounter the
disease yet it affects 40 per cent of the world's population. Malaria is
almost exclusively a plague of the poor, and the disease helps to keep
these people poor, costing the African economy more than $12 billion
every year. In the late 1960s the World Health Organisation abandoned
its plan to eradicate malaria through the use of the insecticide DDT
against the mosquito, and the drug chloroquine which killed the parasite.
Both the mosquito and the parasite became resistant to these agents and
since then there have been no significant breakthroughs in finding new
controls or therapies.

But in 2002, scientists completed the sequence of the genomes of the parasite that causes the most deadly form of malaria, *Plasmodium falciparum*, and the mosquito that transmits it, *Anopheles gambae*. The genome sequences will bring hope to a field of medical research that has been struggling to find treatments and vaccines against a parasite that kills more people than almost any other infectious disease, and that is equalled only by tuberculosis and HIV.

The mosquito and parasite genome projects were initiated independently, by different groups, and have very different histories. The parasite genome has always been seen as the most important in terms of generating new treatments but it was known to have a chemical imbalance in its DNA that made it particularly difficult to work with. All living things have a genome made up of four letters – A, G, C and T. *Plasmodium* DNA has the same letters but, for some unknown reason, 80 per cent of them are A or T. This makes the DNA unstable and difficult to analyse – in fact many scientists thought a sequencing project would be impossible. Despite this, the *Plasmodium* genome project was initiated in 1995. The scale of the task required three different groups to tackle the genome: The Institute of Genome Research (TIGR) and the Stanford Center for Genome Technology in the United States, and the Sanger Institute in the UK. This was an unprecedented collaboration at the time, a bit like General Motors, Ford and Volkswagen working together to make a new car, and in the early days disagreements erupted over who would sequence which bits of the genome and how the data would be analysed. However, the importance of the project overcame rivalry in 2001, in a Philadelphia hotel bar where the plan to jointly publish the entire genome was drawn up. The Sanger-TIGR collaboration thus forged forms the basis of most parasite genome projects today.

The *Anopheles* genome project was initiated in 2001, six years after the *Plasmodium* project, and despite having a genome ten times the size of the parasite it was sequenced in a fraction of the time. This phenomenal speed was possible in part because the mosquito had a normal genome, but also because of massive advances in sequencing technology that had occurred in the interval between the projects – these advances were driven by pioneering efforts like the *Plasmodium* project.

The genome sequences do not offer an immediate answer to the disease but they promise to promote malaria research to the fast lane of drug and vaccine discovery, and for the first time scientists are optimistic for the

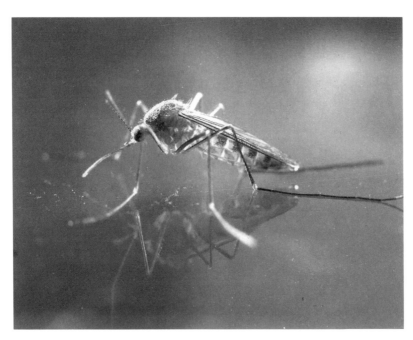

Malarial mosquito: the genetic secrets of a mass murderer.

future. The sequences give researchers a full inventory of the genes that make the parasite and the mosquito. These genes encode proteins which are the building blocks of life and carry out all of the biochemical processes which allow living things to function. The difficulty is knowing what all of the proteins do. A genome sequence is a bit like having a French dictionary when you hardly speak the language: all the words are there but it is hard to decipher what they mean. So how does a genome help? Instead of isolating one gene at a time and finding out what it does, researchers can now look at all of the genes and analyse them in one go using modern, high-throughput, molecular biological techniques. With this information scientists can direct their research to design drugs that will 'knock out' proteins that are unique to the parasite and are not in the human host. These drugs would then be safe to administer to humans but would control the parasite. A similar approach can be used to design safe effective insecticides.

The holy grail of malaria research would be to design a vaccine that could eradicate the disease. Unfortunately the malaria parasite is a master of disguise and is able to hide itself inside red blood cells; it also constantly changes the proteins it exposes to the host's immune system. The genome sequence encodes all of the proteins that interact with the immune system

Genomics

73

and now scientists can test these to see which of them can be used to 'teach' our immune systems to recognize the parasite; these proteins would make good vaccines. Researchers are also trying to identify which mosquito genes may be interacting with the parasite when it is in the insect. If they could understand this they could design chemical sprays that would prevent the mosquito transmitting the parasite.

While the genome sequences herald a huge leap forward in malaria research, the fruits of this investment may be some years away. It takes many years and millions of pounds to take new discoveries from the lab to pharmacy, and it is not clear who will make this investment. As treatments must target the world's poorest people, any vaccine or drug must be cheap and simple to administer if it is to significantly affect the worldwide burden of the disease. Pharmaceutical companies will not make large profits selling malaria treatments to the poor, so future advances are still dependent on handouts from charities and governments. A cure for poverty remains elusive.

Genome sequencing: Wellcome news?

JANE ROGERS

How much more can we learn about ourselves
from mouse DNA? Or rat, zebrafish, frog and pig?

Fifty years ago, in a laboratory in Cambridge, two young men used wires
and cardboard to work out how the DNA molecule was put together.
They discovered the talismanic double helix. Today, in a high-tech,
purpose-built facility a few miles away, six hundred people are bringing
fruit from the seeds sown. The Wellcome Trust Sanger Institute has
decoded a third of the human genome, and half of the nematode worm
– an achievement for which the institute's founder, John Sulston, won
a Nobel award in 2002 – as well as the genomes of many other creatures,
from the laboratory mouse to important human and animal pathogens.
Why? To understand how living things work.

 We stand today at a remarkable point in history. The work of the past fifty years promises – or for some people, threatens – to transform many aspects of human existence. Since Crick and Watson's seminal work, we have discovered how DNA codes for life and we have devised methods to read that code; we have in our hands the tools to understand the genetic contributions to being a human. How have we come to this so quickly? How have scientists helped non-scientists to wrestle with this knowledge? What lies ahead?

Cambridge celebrates 50 years of DNA in 2003

James Watson, Francis Crick and Maurice Wilkins won the 1962 Nobel prize for physiology and medicine for deciphering the structure of the double helix in 1953. The university claims all three as Cambridge prizes (Wilkins, of King's College, London, was a student there and later a professor).

Thereafter, thanks to molecular biology, Nobel prizes stuck to Cambridge like feathers to glue. John Kendrew and Max Perutz, both players in Watson's science thriller *The Double Helix*, won chemistry awards, also in 1962. Frederick Sanger, having won one Nobel in 1958, went on to collect another in 1980 for showing how to 'read' the DNA code and for making the human genome project possible. Fellow of Clare College and cancer researcher Tim Hunt shared a Nobel in 2001.

In 2002 Sir John Sulston, begetter of the Wellcome Trust Sanger Institute and leading player in both the nematode worm and human genome projects, shared a Nobel with the South-African born Sydney Brenner, now in California but fellow of King's College, Cambridge. Their prize, also shared with Robert Horvitz of the Massachusetts Institute of Technology (in Cambridge, Massachusetts), was for 'discoveries concerning genetic regulation of organ development and programmed cell death'. Sir John made the point that discoveries should be shared. 'We gave all our results to others as soon as we had them. From sharing, discovery is accelerated in the community.'

At the end of 2002, an initial analysis of the entire mouse genome, determined from a draft of the sequence, was published in *Nature*. We can think of the mouse genome as a phrasebook to help us in a foreign language – in this case the language in our genes, the human 'book of life'. Because we now have two sets of almost complete information coding for two mammals, we can translate more easily from one genome to another.

By the time this book is published, the reference human genome sequence will be 'finished', with an error rate of fewer than one in ten thousand bases. The reference sequence is not the sequence of any one individual – all human genomes differ from each other, typically by 3 million bases; the reference will provide a sequence against which variations in individuals can be measured. The Human Genome Project, funded in the UK by the Wellcome Trust, will then have produced the archival information necessary in order to serve biomedicine in the future.

Production of this resource has often been depicted as a race between private and public efforts. This is wrong. It has not been a race, but a battle to ensure that the tools to speed biomedical research were available to all, freely and without restriction. There is one certain way to speed discovery and that is to share the information that makes invention possible. In the race to improve human health, openness matters, and an international collaboration worked to ensure that this finished reference sequence was available in the public domain.

Within the next ten years, we can now expect to read the DNA sequence of most organisms that are used routinely to understand how different parts of animals work at the cellular level. These will include the genomes of the rat, zebrafish, frog, chicken, cow and pig. This, of course, will still represent only a tiny fraction of the panoply of life on Earth. It is as if an army of medieval monks had transcribed religious tracts painstakingly, and a paragraph at a time, before assembling them into one almost magical volume.

But the major task lies ahead. As with any religious tract, the hard work lies in interpretation, and vast armies of scholars will be occupied for decades trying to decode the messages in these books of life. For genome sequences are nothing without interpretation and examination, and it is clear that there is an enormous amount to unravel.

DNA is a four-bit linear code – a string of four bases in which the information is encoded in the order, or sequence, of those bases.

In cells, the molecules that do the work are proteins, complex three-dimensional objects which interact with one another to modify behaviour. The DNA provides the instructions for making the proteins in the right places and at the right times, and this results in the hundreds of other molecules that are needed to make cells work. We have learned to understand what the codes for proteins are, but there is an almost unimaginable leap in complexity from the instruction manual to the physical object. As we move to understanding our own genome, the demands for informatics – the software, machines and people to add various layers of interpretation – are increasing. At the Wellcome Trust Sanger Institute, our computer power has increased tenfold over the past five years in order to be able to collect the DNA sequence. But we anticipate a further twentyfold increase will be needed over the next five years in order to collect the information about DNA function.

However, computers are not enough. What they reveal must be validated by experimental evidence. There is scope for individuals to work in depth on single genes or pathways, but there will also be significant benefit from experimental analysis on a large scale. From identifying genes that are mutated in cancer, to measuring levels of individual proteins in normal and diseased cells, high-throughput biology is the most cost-effective means to provide information to biomedical research. Each new method demands detailed analysis of complex data – far more complex than sequence information alone. We are beginning to link DNA sequence with the biological effects on an organism – this is called the phenotype – and that involves full characterization of genomes. In turn, this means not just understanding which sequences code for proteins, but also understanding how regulation occurs. We need to image the levels or movement of proteins in cells, and link laboratory bench observations to real cells in real organisms. One challenge is to refine the means of capturing this information, storing it and making it available in a form that is valuable to researchers, physicians and pathologists. There will be a need for quality standards for the new data sets that are already being generated, so that work in different laboratories and on different continents can be compared.

Of course, this will not stop with the analysis of a single organism. One of the most successful ways to extract information from genomes is to compare them: mouse, for example, with human. In evolution, selective pressure acts on those parts of the genome that are 'important' to the organism in one way or another. Comparison of two genome sequences requires direct comparison of 3 billion bases with 3 billion bases. When this was done for the mouse and human genomes, a range of similarities was found, for few sequences in two genomes are truly identical and most are similar to varying degrees. About 5 per cent of the human and mouse genomes correspond very closely, suggesting these regions have been under pressure not to diverge, and code for molecules that are common to both species.

So how valuable is a new genome sequence? The mouse is a good indicator. Although separated from human by about 70 million years of evolution, the two genomes share about 99 per cent of their genes – counterparts of varying similarity can be found for almost all the genes in the two species. More importantly, 1200 genes unknown to biology were found in the human genome through this comparison. It is important to understand that, although standards are always rising, the ability of computers to predict the location and structure of genes remains imprecise. The best software alone will identify perhaps 50 per cent of genes accurately, though using several programs improves that prediction rate. This figure can be improved again by human annotators, who can compare the genomic sequence with sequences of genes derived from the molecules that are intermediaries in the process of making proteins.

However, having a complete sequence from a related organism provides nature's own gene-identification programme. Genes tend to be conserved (they are the 'important' bits of DNA) and so the pair-wise comparisons will align accurately where genes are the same, or very similar. A comparison of two genomes provides information from a moment in time. If they are too distant, in evolutionary terms, then parts of the gene, or whole genes, will not be similar enough to align; if they are too close, then regions that are not genes will align. Evolution acts at different rates on different regions of the genome – this can be clearly deduced from the mouse–human comparison. To identify regions that differ in their rate of evolution demands comparison between humans and a range of other organisms, some distant and some close.

So now we have massive amounts of DNA sequence and growing amounts of layered information tied to that sequence. To make the most of these genomes, it is important that all the datasets are linked in an accessible fashion. This is the role of Ensembl and similar genome 'browsers'. Ensembl (www.ensembl.org) retrieves the most up-to-date data. Using a browser, it is possible to scroll along a human chromosome from one end to the other and see the positions of genes and their sequences, interspersed amongst the sequence of largely unknown function. It is possible to examine changes in reference sequence. These are the positions of base variations (SNPs – single nucleotide polymorphisms) that have been found in DNA from different people, and which will be indicators of some genetic diseases. There are also links from the sequence to other databases – for example disease gene datasets and protein databases – as well as to other genomes. It is straightforward now to jump from a region of the human genome to the same region in the mouse genome and to compare gene content, gene order and many other features. The demand for Ensembl is such that around thirty organizations around the world – including leading pharmaceutical companies – have downloaded the entire site and operate in-house 'mirrors'. Every minute, 2 million bases of sequence information are downloaded from Ensembl, and it is used by researchers in more than eighty countries.

Has genomics lived up to expectations, or are the stock markets right in revaluing predictions? Biologists, like all scientists, have done the experiments they can do. As Sir Peter Medawar said: 'Science is the art of the soluble.' For biology, this means studying one gene at a time. Already, great strides have been made in identifying genes that are mutated in most monogenic conditions (those that are caused by a mutation in a single gene). Even back when the human genome draft sequence was published in *Nature*, reports of more than fifty genes discovered by researchers using the freely available draft data had already appeared.

One example was the discovery by the Cancer Genome Project (CGP) at the Wellcome Trust Sanger Institute that one gene, BRAF, was mutated in 70 per cent of malignant melanoma cases. Mutations such as that in BRAF are caused by the mutated protein acting as though it was active all the time, rather than turned on only at specific times; in the case of BRAF, the cell divides uncontrollably. This mutated protein exists only in tumour cells. Thus a drug designed to inhibit mutated BRAF protein should be active only against tumour cells. This is a major hope of cancer biology and one that has some support from results with other tumour types. The aim of the CGP is to identify all such mutations from our common cancers over the next five years. If this goal is achieved, all these diseases will become targets for focused research on specific proteins, rather than broader attempts to find generic compounds.

However, many of these diseases are relatively rare conditions, whereas most that rack citizens of the developed world – heart disease, lung disease, asthma – are caused by mutations in more than one gene, interacting with environmental influences. Using the genomes we have collected, and the informatics tools we have developed, we can start taking such diseases to bits, and work out what it is that the suspect genes do – and how to prevent them doing it. Already, genes that may predispose to childhood eczema have been found using the finished sequence of chromosome 20, and others will emerge.

Has the human genome received too much publicity? At the Wellcome Trust Sanger Institute, we have tried not to build a sense of instant achievement in medicine, but to emphasize that we and our partners have laid foundation stones for a new biology that can cope with the complexities of the data generated. When the Human Genome Project was first proposed in the mid 1980s, DNA sequencing cost around $10–20 per base, and to get a few hundred bases took one person a day or two. The entire project was predicated on advances in systems of all types to allow it to succeed. The new genome data is 'pulling' the development of new technologies and software, but the next step (frequently referred to as post-genomics) also depends on new developments.

It was important that the public's attention was grabbed by the emerging sequence. It will change our lives in the near and distant future, and it is vital that citizens can make informed judgements as to which developments serve society best and which should be limited. The double helix will insinuate itself into healthcare, employment, insurance, racism, schooling – into all of our social fabric. We hoped that the announcement in June 2000 would act as a clarion call to the public.

Our results are released to the internet without restriction and our research is published in scientific journals. But these methods are not enough to bring society into debate and into the decision-making process. Carefully phrased public announcements, responsible journalism, openness, public participation, debate and information are needed to help us reach decisions as to what we do with our genome, what we can afford to do with our genome, and who benefits first or most from the research. Genomes are powerful raw materials for good: like fine steel, we must forge them into ploughshares rather than swords.

Mathematics

Mathematicians and the war on terror

KEITH DEVLIN

In 2002, statisticians suddenly found themselves in the front line in the battle against terrorism.

Undoubtedly, the biggest mathematical event during 2002 was the opening of the movie *A Beautiful Mind*, director Ron Howard's fictionalized account of the life of Princeton mathematician John Forbes Nash, winner of the 1994 Nobel prize for economics. The film begins in 1948, with the chairman of the Princeton mathematics department, played by Judd Hirsch, telling the newly arrived class – among them John Nash, played by Russell Crowe – 'It was mathematicians that won the war.' The reference is to code breaking during World War II, in particular the top-secret activities of the small group of mathematicians the British government assembled at Bletchley Park during the late 1940s. These mathematicians were portrayed in another film, *Enigma*, this one a British product, directed by Michael Apted and released in the US a few months after *A Beautiful Mind.*

Such is life in the twenty-first century that fiction outshines reality. But by one of those rare coincidences that arise from time to time, while cinema audiences the world over were overdosing on fictionalized higher mathematics, real life was starting to repeat itself, as the US government called on the mathematical community – the real one – to assist it in fighting a new war: this time, against global terrorism, following the atrocity of 11 September 2001.

In April, the US National Academies' Board on Mathematical Sciences and their Applications (BMSA) organized a two-day, invitation-only workshop called 'The Mathematical Sciences' Role in Homeland Security', hosted by the National Research Council in Washington DC. The aim of the conference was to bring together leading experts in the various areas of mathematics that are likely to be required in fighting international terrorist organizations, with a view to setting a national research agenda to aid the country in combating this new kind of warfare.

Mathematicians from universities, industry, and national laboratories who attended the workshop found themselves rubbing shoulders with senior representatives from the Defense Advanced Research Projects Agency (DARPA), the National Security Agency (NSA), the Centers for Disease Control and Prevention (CDCP), the Directorate of Defense Research and Engineering, and of course the Office of Homeland Security. The topics discussed fell into five general (and overlapping) areas: data mining and pattern recognition, detection and epidemiology of bioterrorist attacks, voice and image recognition, communications and computer security, and data fusion. With increased funding being poured into these topics, they are likely to be the hot areas of mathematical research in the coming decade. At the moment, many of them are unfamiliar to most mathematicians, and they are quite different from the kinds of mathematics that were required to fight wars in the past. Statistical and computational techniques figure heavily in this new kind of strategic mathematics.

Data mining and pattern recognition are relatively new branches of mathematics that look for ways to discover patterns, structure, or associations in large bodies of empirical data, such as financial or travel records. Much of the early research in this area was developed for industrial and commercial purposes, for instance, by banks to detect credit card fraud, by telephone companies to spot unauthorized use of the phone system, and by supermarket chains to identify purchasing patterns. (Why do you think they have those electronically readable loyalty reward cards?) The relevance of this area of research to national security is obvious.

The detection and epidemiology of bioterrorist attacks involves a number of lines of mathematical research. The development of mathematical models of how diseases spread is one of the examples best known to mathematicians – known in part because simple scenarios form standard examples in calculus classes. In fact, within days of the September 11 attacks on the World Trade Center towers and the Pentagon, researchers at Los Alamos National Laboratory had taken a mathematical model of traffic flow they had been developing and applied it to predict the likely spread of disease following a possible bioterrorist attack. There is significant scope for further research into the mathematics of how biological and chemical agents spread.

Another area where mathematics will be important in countering a biological or chemical attack is in early detection that such an attack has in fact taken place. In the initial stages, it can be hard to differentiate between a malicious attack with a dangerous weapon and a naturally occurring outbreak of a common agent. The available data is almost always noisy, creating a need for better techniques to integrate and fuse data to identify patterns, determine sources, increase confidence, and predict the spread of infectious or chemical agents, in order that the available counter-agents or containment methods may be brought to bear in the most timely and efficient fashion. Mathematics is likely to turn out to be one of the main weapons in fighting this new kind of war.

Voice and image recognition was a further topic on the table in Washington. Today's terrorists operate globally, maintaining contact by telephone and the internet. Identifying the occasional key telephone conversation among the millions that take place daily can only be done (if it can be done at all) using sophisticated automation, with monitoring systems that are able to break down voices and words into digital patterns that can be scanned for keywords. This requires the development of new algorithms to monitor communications channels in real time to provide defence authorities with early warnings of a potential threat. Similarly, methods need to be developed for the automated screening of images sent over the internet, to look for messages embedded in pictures, a technique, known as steganography, believed to have been used by the September 11 terrorists. New and more sophisticated mathematical techniques for image processing and recognition will also be required to identify potential terrorists involved in suspicious activities and to improve screening at airports and other checkpoints.

Communications and computer security was the only thread of the conference that connected attendants with their cryptography predecessors at Bletchley Park. But the situation today is very different from the one that prevailed in the 1940s. With secure encryption systems now widely available to security forces and terrorists alike, the focus has shifted to the overall integrity of communication and computer systems. A secure cryptosystem becomes worthless if an enemy can break into your computer or disrupt the network. There is thus a pressing need for taking a broad look at computers and computer networks to examine their vulnerabilities and develop ways to defend them, including by the early detection of an attack. New methods for analysing internet traffic are likely to be important in this new area of cyber warfare.

Data fusion, yet another topic at the conference, is the process of synthesizing information from diverse sources in order to make prudent decisions. At present there is little by way of a reliable mathematical framework to support this kind of activity. Current practitioners make largely ad hoc use of statistics, probability, decision theory, graph theory, and tools from artificial intelligence and expert systems design. The relevant parts of these disciplines need to be merged into at least a compatible toolkit, if not a coherent theory. There are enormous theoretical challenges to be overcome in order to make progress in this now crucial area.

One of the most promising techniques going into the data fusion mix builds on the work of an eighteenth-century English clergyman, Thomas Bayes. A Presbyterian minister who did mathematics as a hobby, Bayes showed how to make an estimate that a particular event will take place, and combine it with hard evidence in order to obtain a better estimate. More precisely, you start with an initial estimate of the probability that the event will occur and an estimate of the reliability of the evidence. The method then tells you how to combine those two figures – in a precise, mathematical way – to give a new estimate of the event's probability in the light of the evidence.

In some highly constrained situations, both initial estimates may be entirely accurate, and in such cases Bayes's method will give you the correct answer. In a more typical real-life situation, you don't have exact figures, but as long as the initial estimates are reasonably good, then the method will give you a better estimate of the probability that the event of interest will occur. In the words of some statisticians, it's 'mathematics on top of common sense'. In the hands of an expert in the domain under consideration, someone who is able to assess all the available evidence reliably, Bayes's method can be a powerful tool.

Because of the way the method combines mathematical precision with human guesswork, statisticians ignored Bayesian inference for many years. It was really only in the 1990s that, driven by the commercial pressures of product development, the method began to come into greater use. For example, chemists nowadays make regular use of a software system that employs Bayesian methods to improve the resolution of nuclear magnetic resonance (NMR) spectrum data. They need such data to work out the molecular structure of substances they wish to analyse. The system uses Bayes's formula to combine the new data from the NMR device with existing NMR data, a procedure that can improve the resolution of the data by several orders of magnitude. Other recent uses of Bayesian inference are in the evaluation of new drugs and medical treatments, the analysis of human DNA to identify particular genes, and in analysing police arrest data to see if any officers have been targeting one particular ethnic group.

Then there are the newer uses in fighting urban terrorism. Armed with powerful computers to handle all the data, security experts use Bayesian inference to prioritize potential threats facing the nation. With national security, there are so many sources of information to be assessed that Bayes's theorem has to be applied many times in succession, in the systematic form of what is known as a Bayesian network. This method was developed in the late 1980s by the mathematician Judea Pearl of the University of California at Los Angeles. In a twist of fate, Pearl's own son Danny, a journalist, was murdered by terrorists in Pakistan in 2002.

In the past few years, private defence contractors have been developing commercial software systems that implement Bayesian networks for risk assessment, an industry that has grown dramatically since September 11. One such system, Site Profiler, developed by Digital Sandbox of Reston, Virginia, when subjected to field trials early in 2001, flagged the Pentagon as being particularly likely to be the target of an attack – a result that at the time was regarded as wildly unlikely.

The Washington workshop was not expected to provide answers to any pressing questions. That was not the purpose. As with the war on terrorism itself, we are in the early days of what will certainly be a long haul. The Washington workshop was intended merely to draw up a roadmap of where the nation wants to go and how it might get there. Much of the work that has to be done will not be 'hard, elegant' mathematics of the kind that many mathematicians view as a thing of beauty. (Although history tells us that there is a high probability that this effort will lead to such mathematics as an unintended side effect.) Consequently, there are likely to be few public rewards or accolades for those who choose to engage in such projects. At least, not until Hollywood gets round to making today's real-life backroom efforts into tomorrow's mass entertainment.

Why genomics could be a disaster for medical science

DAVID HORROBIN

Do fifty years of DNA add up to a golden year
for the geneticists?

Triumphalism about molecular biology, genomics and the human
genome project is an increasingly pervasive theme in biomedical science.
Beginning soon after Watson and Crick deciphered the structure of DNA,
it has become progressively more dominant, reaching a crescendo over
the past five years. Primary scientific literature, popular science magazines
and the general media have united in a near-unanimous chorus of praise
concerning the magnitude of the scientific achievement, and the
supposedly dramatic effects this is going to have on human health.

I hope this article will make almost everyone who reads it angry.
It will make the genomics enthusiasts angry because it documents some
of the ways in which they have corrupted scientific endeavour and

destroyed the real hope of progress. It will make other readers angry because of the ways in which they have been deceived.

From the 1930s to the 1960s, biomedical science bore some resemblance to an integrated whole. There were researchers working at every level of biological organization, from subcellular biochemistry to whole cells, isolated organs and whole animals, as well as physiologists and clinicians working with humans. Each group recognized the importance of the others and there was a constant flow of information up and down the ladder of organizational complexity. Surprisingly frequently, it was the clinicians who made the novel and unexpected observations which were then interpreted and analysed by scientists working at simpler organizational levels, and then applied back to human health by the physiologists and clinicians.

In terms of the contribution of science to human health this was a golden age. Antibiotics, the widespread application of new vaccines such as that for polio, new medicines for a wide range of diseases including high blood pressure, depression, schizophrenia and anxiety, and a reduction in tropical diseases such as malaria and and sleeping sickness to nadirs not seen before or since, all occurred during this productive time. Anyone receiving the best medical care in 1965 was incomparably better off than anyone receiving the best medical care in 1930. The successes arose because solutions came from many different levels. Public health specialists working at social, cultural, educational and economic levels were largely responsible for the control of malaria and sleeping sickness. Cell culture specialists working with clinicians solved polio. Microbiologists working with chemists and clinicians eliminated the threat posed by most infections. Physiologists working with pharmacologists and again clinicians created the dramatic progress in cardiovascular, renal, respiratory medicine and endocrinology. Clinicians and pharmacologists working with chemists produced the revolution in psychiatry that enabled so many patients to leave hospitals. In every field, progress depended on a constant exchange of knowledge, passing up and down the chain of complexity.

But starting in the 1960s, with increasing confidence in the 1970s and 1980s and with supreme arrogance in the 1990s, the molecular biologists and genomics specialists took over biomedical science. Everything was to be understood – and understood completely – at the molecular genomic level. Everything was to be reduced, not just to the cell but to the genome. Journals and grant-giving bodies came to be dominated by arrogant reductionists who were scathing about the complexity of whole-organ, whole-animal and especially whole-human studies, which were seen as messy, unscientific and too full of uncontrolled variability to be interpretable. Repeatedly, clinical and physiological studies lost out, and progressively their research communities were destroyed. Almost no one now works on whole animals, looking at how they function in an integrated way. Many have documented the destruction of clinical research, which has steadily moved away from pathophysiology and has become dominated by reductionist genomics specialists. We now have an almost wholly reductionist biomedical community which repeatedly makes exaggerated claims about how it is going to revolutionize medical treatment – and which equally repeatedly fails to achieve anything. And the reductionists fail because of astounding ignorance about the real complexity of human beings and their diseases.

What is the evidence for such a sweeping statement? The first genetic disease to be fully defined in molecular terms was sickle-cell disease, the abnormality of the haemoglobin in human red blood cells which causes such devastation in African and Afro-American communities. In molecular terms this is the simplest and best understood of all genetic problems. A single abnormality in a single protein causes the trouble. The abnormal protein was identified by Pauling in the 1940s, the precise molecular defect was identified by Ingram in the 1950s, and the three-dimensional structure of the protein was defined by Kendrew and Perutz in the 1960s. Yet what has been the clinical impact of this wonderfully precise molecular knowledge which we have now had for over forty years? Precisely nothing. The clinical picture of the disease is enormously complex and cannot yet be understood in terms of the molecular biology. A comprehensive review of the pathophysiology of sickle-cell disease, published in 2002, stated 'This complex disease underscores the intellectual and practical distance between the determination of molecular genetics and effective clinical application and therapeutics.'

Or take human therapeutics as a whole. Whereas diagnostics and surgery have made extraordinary advances since the mid 1960s, the advances in medical treatment, while trumpeted widely, have been minimal. In only two areas, stomach and duodenal ulceration and organ transplantation has medical treatment improved dramatically.

- Life expectancy at birth in sub-Saharan Africa is now estimated at 47 years, according to 2002 World Health Organisation data. Without Aids, it would be around 62 years.

- About 70 per cent of all cases of HIV infection (28 million out of a worldwide total of 40 million) are concentrated in Africa. The continent is home to 10 per cent of the world's population.

- One child in 100 born in sub-Saharan Africa is likely die of pneumococcal infections such as meningitis, septicaemia, and pneumonia.

- In 2000, the US spent $3724 per person on healthcare. Somalia spent $11.

In almost every other field, people being medically treated now are little better off than people who received the best available treatment in 1965.

Take three examples. In psychiatry, to read the literature from the pharmaceutical industry, one would think that the treatments of depression and schizophrenia have been transformed. But the US Food and Drug Administration (FDA) has recently released its databases on all the drugs it has approved. In both depression and schizophrenia the outcomes of treatment with drugs introduced in the 1990s are very slightly worse than the outcomes with drugs introduced in the 1950s and 1960s. Side-effect profiles are different but not necessarily better.

In the cardiovascular field again one would think we had made huge advances, judging from the hype. Modern cardiovascular drug developers pride themselves on the vast trials they employ to prove the efficacy of their treatments – five thousand, ten thousand or even twenty thousand patients may be involved – and the media seem to be impressed by the sheer size of the studies. But to anyone who understands statistics, the need for such enormous trials is the giveaway. They are needed only because the effects of the new drugs show such trivial advantages over the old. The advantages are so small that trials with smaller numbers would never be able to demonstrate the treatment's value.

Or take cancer. We have indeed made dramatic progress in a very limited range of rare cancers – the leukaemias, lymphomas and testicular tumours. But even in these cases, many of the drugs used were introduced before 1965. We have simply learned to use them better and apply them more widely. Real efficacy in any of the common cancers has proved elusive.

Further evidence of the failure of therapeutic research can be seen in the fortunes of the pharmaceutical industry. From the 1940s to the 1970s they introduced a stream of truly revolutionary new compounds which changed the way medicine is practised. But as molecular biology took hold, and the contributions of the clinicians, pharmacologists and physiologists were downgraded, the flow of new products slowed. And then in a mad capitulation to the new reductionist science, in the late 1980s and 1990s the companies bought into molecular biology and genomics in a big way. They fired most of their physiologists, pharmacologists and clinical researchers, losing their knowledge of complex biological systems. They spent almost unbelievable sums on genomics with a result of almost nothing. The rates of important new drug discoveries have progressively fallen, in spite of an annual R&D spend by the top companies of around $30 billion every year. In consequence, the valuations of giant corporations like Merck, GSK, AstraZeneca, Bristol-Myers Squibb and many more have fallen by 20–50 per cent, or even more. Both the FDA and its European equivalent, the EMEA, have just announced that the numbers of new drug applications in 2002 have fallen well below their historically low 2001 level. It is clear that there has been a massive corporate failure which is directly attributable to the buy-in to molecular biology and genomics. Yet the scientists, with Ozymandian arrogance, still insist that everything is OK and if we the public just continue to provide money all will turn out right in the end.

The problem with these people is that their cleverness is deep but very narrow. A good example of both the arrogant cleverness and the ignorance is the hype surrounding the malaria genome project. This is indeed a brilliant technical achievement but the claims that it will lead to a solution to malaria in five years are absurd. Malaria is enormously more complex than sickle-cell disease and the investigators who announced their discovery seemed to have no understanding of that complexity. In a caustic letter to *The Times*, veteran malaria expert Brian Taylor pointed out that, far from a single type of mosquito being a malaria vector, there were over 65 known species involved. The molecular biologists making their dramatic claims did not even seem to be aware of this elementary fact. This is perhaps not surprising, since entomology is one of the whole-organism sciences which has been largely destroyed by the voracious appetite of the genomics people for the available biomedical scientific funds.

There is no evidence whatsoever that genomic medicine is going to be more successful in any disease than it has been with sickle-cell disease. Anyone familiar with medical research funding knows the disgraceful campaigns which were waged in the 1970s and 1980s by scientists hunting the genes for such diseases as cystic fibrosis and muscular dystrophy, and a range of other genetic disorders. Give us the money, we'll find the gene, and then your problems will be solved, was in essence the message the researchers gave to the families and their supporters. The money was found, the genes were found, and then came nothing but a stunned contemplation of the sheer complexity of the problem, which many clinicians had understood all along. There is indeed one abnormal cystic fibrosis gene, for instance, but within that gene, far from the single simple abnormality of sickle-cell disease, there are now over a thousand known, different protein defects. The complex diseases, like diabetes, or arthritis, or most psychiatric or cardiovascular diseases, are likely to involve interactions between dozens of genes, each as complex as is the single gene for cystic fibrosis. The idea that genomics is going to make a major contribution to human health in the near future is laughable. But the tragedy is that the whole-organism biologists and clinicians who might have helped to unravel the complexity have almost all gone.

Just over forty years ago, when I was a medical student, my tutor at Balliol College, Oxford, Sandy Ogston, made me spend a precious half term studying comparative physiology. I had to learn how camels survive, how seals dive and how polar bears deal with the cold. I also was young and arrogant, enamoured of the modern techniques of cell culture and captivated by the early work in molecular biology. I protested to Sandy that all this animal stuff was a complete waste of time. He replied, 'An isolated cell, or an isolated organ cannot plod across the desert or dive to a hundred feet. If you are going to be a good doctor you need to be able to think in an integrated way about how all the systems work together. That is why I am torturing you with comparative physiology.'

He was, of course, right, and during forty years in clinical research that half term has proved more valuable than anything else I learned as a medical student.

Sandy's concern is still relevant. Can you imagine an isolated gene climbing Everest, or even going to the supermarket to do the shopping? Narrow cleverness is getting us nowhere. If genomics is to deliver even a fraction of the promised benefits to human health, a balanced research effort must be restored, and we must drastically reduce the proportion of the available funds devoted to molecular biology.

Depression: we think as we feel

LEWIS WOLPERT

The brain may be more a creature of its moods than anyone expected.

Emotions dominate how we behave. Yet understanding emotion, like any brain function, is no simple undertaking, as I learned from a recent meeting on this topic at the Banbury Center at Cold Spring Harbor on Long Island. There is now, I concluded, reason to believe that almost all our voluntary behaviour is influenced by our emotions. This is in contrast to the tendency to focus on what have been called the basic emotions – anger, disgust, surprise, fear, anxiety, happiness – all of which have very distinct facial responses and which can be evoked by specific stimuli. But it is now becoming clear that emotions are like the ether: they are everywhere. If I scratch my nose, it is to relieve a minor emotional state of discomfort, and pain, hunger and sleepiness clearly reflect an emotional state. However there are some authorities, such as

- Depression is among the leading causes of disability.
- Depression is the fourth leading contribution to the global burden of disease and will rise to second place by 2020.
- It affects 121 million people, worldwide.
- One man in 16, and one woman in 20, will suffer a depressive episode in any given year.
- Less than 25 per cent of people suffering from depression have access to effective treatments.
- Along with schizophrenia – which affects 24 million people worldwide – depressive disorders are responsible for 60 per cent of all suicides.

Antonio Damasio, neurologist at the University of Iowa and author of *The Feeling of What Happens*, who take a somewhat different view, and would not accept pain, for example, as an emotion.

But why are we not zombies, why have emotions at all? We need some way of knowing what to pursue and what to learn to avoid, and emotions do just this – they provide an abstract representation of values. Emotions are part of our genetic inheritance, they are programmed into our brain when we are developing as an embryo, and probably cannot be learned. They have been selected in evolution to guide our actions. One cannot but be struck by the fact that fear of spiders and snakes is widespread, but no children develop a fear of cars or electric plugs, no matter how often they are warned about them by their parents. In studies in which subjects have to find a particular element within a picture, they are faster at finding a dead animal than, say, a bear.

Most learning depends on reward and punishment, which are again based on positive and negative emotions respectively. For example, a colleague reported getting ill after eating watermelon for the first time – finding it delicious – and then having too much wine. On the next occasion he saw a watermelon it seemed disgusting to him. There is evidence that people freeze at the sight of a snake even before they are aware of it. The emotional response may be to ensure that they recall the sight and so learn how to avoid danger in the future. However there is evidence that events and objects experienced just before an intense emotional event are very difficult to recall – a particular problem for witnesses of a highly emotional event.

Almost all learned actions are due to the satisfaction of an emotion, one that rewards or punishes. Is there any voluntary action that is not essentially driven to satisfy an emotion (if you count emotions as varied as discomfort, sleepiness and anger)? Emotion parses the world into adaptive challenges. Every thought triggers or is triggered by an emotion.

Particular attention has focused on one brain structure as playing a fundamental role in emotion: the amygdala, which is just above the roof of the mouth. A patient without an amygdala has almost no emotional responses, except for the recall of earlier events. Most experiments have been related to the emotion of fear, and patients with lesions in the amygdala have difficulty recognizing the emotional facial expressions of others, particularly fear. In normal subjects, activation of the amygdala occurs when the subject is presented with facial expressions of fear; curiously it is the left amygdala that is most affected. But the amygdala, important as it is, is but one of many brain structures involved in processing emotions.

Since emotions are part of our evolutionary and genetic heritage they can, like all other bodily functions, go badly wrong. The most common malfunction is sadness, which is related to depression. Depression is now considered by the World Health Organisation to be an illness that causes more distress in terms of economic cost and morbidity than almost any other. In the United Kingdom it affects about 10 per cent of the population. There is no simple diagnosis of depression, but characteristics include fatigue, sense of worthlessness, too much or too little sleep, suicidal thoughts, and automatic negative attributions and responses to everything. It is not an easy illness to understand, as is true for any human behaviour, normal or abnormal, that involves complex brain functions. It is generally accepted that depression is an affective disorder – that something has gone wrong with the person's emotions and feelings – and so to understand depression it is essential to understand sadness.

Sadness is a basic and universal emotion with a particular facial expression which clearly has, as Darwin recognized, an important role in social communication. Unfortunately sadness has received very little study compared to fear, though it has been studied in infants, particularly in relation to being left alone by their mothers; its function at this stage is to maintain attachment. Sadness is usually triggered by a loss of some sort, from death of a loved one, through loss of money, to failure to achieve a goal. The passage from sadness to depression is not well understood but genetic factors are responsible for about half of an individual's vulnerability. That depression can have a purely biological basis is illustrated by the induction of depression in patients with Cushings disease, who have abnormally high levels of the stress hormone cortisol. Again, alpha interferon is a drug given to patients with hepatitis and this can cause severe depression, so they are given antidepressants at the same time.

In depressed patients the amygdala again plays an important role and the left amygdala has an increased level of activity. This may be

Austin,
January 2003.

due to a reduction of activity in the prefrontal cortex where there is also a loss of special cells that support the nerve cells. There are also reports that the hippocampus, so important for making memories, is smaller in depressed patients.

Low serotonin has also been linked to depression. Serotonin is a molecule that is released at the synapse – the junction – of many nerve cells in the brain, in order to transmit a signal from one nerve cell to the next. Several antidepressants act, apparently, by blocking the transporter system which removes serotonin from the synapse back into the cell, and so increasing its concentration in the synapse. But there is a network of interactions controlling the level of serotonin inside the nerve cell that includes the level of serotonin synthesis within the cell. New support for the role of low levels of serotonin being linked to depression is based on quite typical genetic differences between individuals for the control of serotonin levels. There are variations in the control region of the gene that codes for the transporter protein. This variation results in different levels of synthesis of the transporter, and high levels of synthesis are associated with increased anxiety and depression, presumably as there is less serotonin in the synapse. By contrast, mice that have been genetically engineered to have no transporter at all, and so should have high levels of serotonin in their synapses, show higher levels of anxiety.

Good progress, but there is clearly a long way still to go in understanding emotion and depression, largely due to the complexity of the network of interacting nerve cells in the brain. Models of neural networks with just a few hundred units have shown that they can be made to recognize handwriting and even faces. But understanding how they work, particularly when they go wrong, is exceptionally difficult. And the brain has billions of such units. Interesting times lie ahead.

How the brain handles numbers

BRIAN BUTTERWORTH

Birds do it, apes do it, even uneducated frogs do it,
but some children just cannot count.

It's hard to imagine what the world would be like if we didn't understand numbers. Suppose you couldn't count the number of players in your team, couldn't see that eleven players is more than ten, couldn't tell that when your team scores five goals and the opponents score four, you win. Suppose that prices were meaningless symbols, that money and change were mysteries, and that dates and times formed a constant puzzle... But where does our ability to understand these numbers come from?

Take a moment to reflect on the question. If you are like most people I've spoken to (there have been no proper surveys) you will answer that numbers and arithmetic are just one of those things you learnt in school – perhaps one of the more boring things. Most of us have forgotten the prior coaching on our mother's knee. Rare indeed is the English child who has not had her toes counted and has not played 'One, two, three, hup'. Some 40 per cent of all English nursery rhymes contain counting words. (I owe this particular number to educationalist, Sir Christopher Ball.) Is it really just a matter of teaching, perhaps with a little intelligence thrown in? In the past year, we have begun to find some answers.

Our understanding of number turns out to be slap-bang in the middle of one of the key debates in the whole study of human nature, a debate that goes back to Plato: does our understanding depend on innate systems of knowledge, or does it depend on our experiences? Nowadays, we express this in rather different language, and our investigative techniques go beyond Platonic dialectic. We talk about coding for brain systems in the genome, about the interactions between genetic and environmental factors, and how to assay the balance between the two. And, of course, we do scientific experiments.

The classical experimental way to establish that a cognitive capacity is innate, is to study what humans can do before they have had chance to learn, that is, when they are infants. Can we find evidence that infants understand numbers? Three years ago, when I published *The Mathematical Brain*, I thought we knew the answer. There had been twenty years of experimentation to show that infants can detect a change in the number of objects in visual array, at least for 'numerosities'

- US scientists reported in *Science* on 9 August 2002 that, at five months, babbling infants opened the right side of the mouth wider than the left, indicating action in the left side of the brain, where language is processed.

- With new software and a virtual reality glove, potential parents may 'touch' their unborn child. Expectant father Tom Anderson of Novint Technologies, New Mexico tested e-touch equipment that converts an ultrasound scan into a sense of feeling. 'It was such an incredible moment,' he said.

- Six-month-old babies are so tuned-in to faces that they can distinguish between two monkeys as easily as between two adult humans. Nine-month-old babies and adult humans are good at recognizing human faces, but both groups failed the monkey test.

Neuroscience

(the number of objects in a collection) up to about three or four. It didn't matter whether the objects stayed in the same position or were moving about, or indeed, whether the objects themselves changed. Of course, we cannot ask infants to count out loud, so experimenters made use of the fact that infants look longer at the unexpected. If you show an infant two objects, then another two objects, then another two, she will start to lose interest in twoness and look less at each successive display. If you then change the number of objects, interest perks up and the infant looks longer.

Infants of six months were also thought to be able to add and subtract, amazing as this may seem. Here is the experimental task, designed by Arizona psychologist Karen Wynn: you show the infant a doll; hide the doll behind a screen; then show a second doll going behind the screen. Will the baby think, 'Ha, one doll and another doll makes two dolls?' That is, will she construct an arithmetical expectation that one plus one equals two? So, when the screen is removed, will the baby look longer if there is only one doll or three dolls? It turns out that this is exactly what happens, and this experiment has been repeated with many variations by other scientists in other laboratories. Similarly, Wynn was able to demonstrate infant subtraction. The baby was shown two dolls, which were then hidden behind a screen. The baby saw a hand reach behind the screen and remove one doll. The baby looked longer at displays of two dolls or no dolls than the expected one doll.

Now when you change the number of objects shown to an infant, all sorts of other factors also change. For example, if the objects were all red, the total quantity of redness the infant could see would also change. We also know that infants pay particular attention to the edges of objects, and when the number of objects increases, then the total length of the edges also increases; and infants may be responding to the change in length rather than to a change in number. Even in Wynn's task, where the baby is forming an expectation on the basis of mental representations rather than a single display – she must imagine what is happening behind the screen – she could be forming representations of continuous quantities rather than numerosities. When a second doll is added, she may think 'Ha, more doll-like stuff', and when a doll is removed, she may think, 'Ha, less doll-like stuff' and form her expectations on the basis of these non-numerical dimensions of the displays.

Naturally, scientists have tried to control for these dimensions, to ensure that the infant is responding to number and not to continuous quantity or edges. We certainly have mechanisms for estimating the overall size of things, for answering the question 'How much (stuff)?' Do we therefore really need a separate mechanism for answering the question 'How many (things)?' This is the problem that has been exercising infant researchers in 2002.

It turns out that it is precisely the technical problem of separating stuff from things that has recently called in doubt some of the earlier experiments. One striking set of experiments by Lisa Feigenson and colleagues, at New York University and MIT, suggests that babies do respond to extent but not to numerosity as such, when these are pitted against each other. Feigenson argues that what babies do is keep a kind of running total of the total quantity of relevant stuff – in this case, total surface area – as they view the array of objects.

When the number of objects is greater than about four, babies seem sensitive to total quantity. They notice a change in numerosity from 8 to 16 objects (or 16 to 8), though not from 8 to 12 (or 12 to 8). For these continuous quantities, a large ratio difference (about 2:1) is what gets noticed.

However, in another intriguing study in 2002, by Karen Wynn and colleagues, total surface area and total amount of edge were controlled in a very clever way. Each 'object' consisted of an array of dots, all of the same size. Babies knew that a group of dots constituted an object because they all moved together, and coherent motion is an extraordinarily powerful cue to objecthood. This meant they could be shown four groups of three dots, three groups of four dots, or two groups of eight dots, and each display would be visually equivalent: the only thing that changed would be the number of groups. With this design, Wynn found that babies of five months did indeed respond to changes in number.

Now there is more to our concept of number than simply being able to recognize that displays have different numerosities. That is, we are not able only to recognize the twoness of a display, or the fourness, we also know that four is not only different from two but bigger than it. A set of numerosity four contains a set of numerosity two. It turns out that pre-linguistic infants, though now about eleven months, can discriminate between increasing numerosities (again of dot arrays) and decreasing numerosities.

Neuroscience

So, have scientists determined whether babies in the first year of life are sensitive just to 'how much stuff', or also to 'how many things'? In the real world, number and continuous quantity correlate, so if the human genome contains instructions to build a brain circuit for detecting and manipulating small numerosities (the number of things in a collection), it would make sense for it not to worry about separating number from continuous quantity. Now there will be times when there is a conflict. In foraging, for example, one big apple could be more nutritious than three small ones and it would make sense to prioritize volume rather than number.

One possible solution to the theoretical conflict is that we have two brain mechanisms, one for number and one for extent, and it may be that in some cases of conflict the continuous quantity cue is more powerful, while in other cases the numerosity cue is stronger. However, there is still one fundamental question to which no one has a very satisfactory answer: what do these mechanisms have to do with adult arithmetical abilities? Are they really proto-arithmetical capacities which we build on as we come into contact with the culture of number – the culture of counted toes and nursery rhymes? Supportive evidence would come from examining the brain activity of babies. If they use the same structures, or parts of the same structures, as adults do when adding or subtracting, then this would be supportive evidence.

We now have a very good idea of the circuits for numerical activities. Stanislas Dehaene in Paris has compiled a composite picture from functional brain imaging which maps the brain regions that show up in all or most numerical tasks. The critical one seems to be in a specialized slice of the IPS (Intraparietal Sulcus – a long fold in the cortex above and behind the ears). Our team in London has started to find evidence that the right-hand IPS may carry out more primitive tasks, such as estimating the number of dots in an array, while the left IPS may be responsible for calculating. This fits in with evidence from brain-damaged patients, where it has been known for many years that damage to the left parietal lobe, but not the right, affects calculating abilities, while damage to the right affects some kinds of estimation.

Do babies use the IPS? We don't know. It is technically difficult and ethically questionable to use functional brain imaging to find out. Other brain-mapping techniques do not have the requisite spatial resolution. But we do have a source of indirect evidence.

Some non-human species appear to have similar abilities to human babies. Hauser has discovered that monkeys in the wild – if you can get their attention – will respond to Wynn's arithmetic task just like infants. And there have been many studies of birds, rats, monkeys and apes, going back over fifty years, demonstrating that they can learn to carry out tasks that depend on recognizing and discriminating between numerosities. But finding similar behaviours isn't enough to show an evolutionary story that connects these behaviours. After all, both birds and bees fly, but avian flight isn't descended from apian flight, or even from a common ancestor. We need to show that the structures involved have an evolutionary relationship. Do these animals use an equivalent brain region to humans?

Let me begin my answer with a cautionary tale. 2002 produced the first study of cells that appear to need no training to be sensitive to number, and are active in the course of the animals' ordinary activity. Frogs and toads use croaking to attract mates and deter same-sex competition. Gary Rose of the University of Utah found that cells in their brains were narrowly tuned to the number of croaks in each phrase that the animal heard. So there would be a cell that responded to one croak per phrase, another that responded to two, and so on up to about five. However, the frog's brain is very different from our own, and the cells that Rose and his team studied were not in the cortex at all (the frog doesn't have the mammalian-style layer of cortical cells), but in a mid-brain structure specialized for hearing. It is therefore unlikely that our own and frogs' brains descended from a common reptilian ancestor, since the brain systems are very different. But it does seem that a sensitivity to numerosities, like flight, can be a useful thing to have.

But 2002 did produce the first evidence from species that are not too distantly related to us, and which certainly have brain structures homologous with our own. A team in Japan trained monkeys to pull a lever a certain number of times and studied the activity in individual brain cells while they did this. They reported to *Nature* this year on the activity of cells in the IPS. These cells were tuned to just a particular number, and would respond less if the monkey made fewer or more pulls than the target.

Put this study together with those on human infants, and we begin to find solid support for hard-wired circuits specialized for discriminating between and thinking about numerosities. If these circuits do exist, then the instructions for building them are located somewhere in the human genome. For some capacities, such as seeing the world in colour, we have now identified the specific brain region and the genes responsible for them. But we also know that sometimes there is a mutation in the gene that leads to a deficit in the capacity – colour blindness, for example. Indeed, the existence of selective deficits in colour vision has been the basis of our understanding of the normal ability to see the world in colour.

If numerical capacities are analogous to colour vision, then we should find people with a specific deficit – a kind of 'number blindness'. It turns out that this condition not only exists – it's called 'dyscalculia' – but that is a hidden epidemic that affects some 5 per cent of the population – a prevalence similar to dyslexia. At the moment, much less is known about dyscalculia than dyslexia, and many schools and educational authorities have yet to recognize it, though the government, to its credit, has recently issued guidelines on dyscalculia and the National Numeracy Strategy.

Can we tie dyscalculia to an abnormality in one part of the brain? There has been only one study of dyscalculics' brains, and that was recently reported in the journal *Brain* by Elizabeth Isaacs and her colleagues at Great Ormond Street Hospital. For many years, they had been studying premature babies with very low birth weight. Most of these babies grow up to have normal cognitive abilities, but the researchers identified one group, by now adolescents, who were normal in every respect except on simple arithmetic. The brains of this group differed from the brains of a matched group of controls, also of very low birth weight, in just one region: the left IPS – exactly where Dehaene and colleagues and other teams have located the circuits implicated in numerosity tasks.

Dyscalculics do not have to try very hard to imagine what it is like to be unable to understand numbers. This is their everyday lot: shopping is an embarrassment since they don't understand what the prices mean, how much to offer at the till or whether they are getting the correct change; times and dates can be a recurring problem; for children in primary school, the struggle with Numeracy Hour is a daily humiliation. Eight- and nine-year-old dyscalculic children told us that they couldn't understand even the ideas that introduced each hour, that they felt stupid, that teachers and parents thought they were stupid, that smarter children picked on them. Many spent the hour in avoidance activities such as going to the toilet, sharpening pencils, looking for rubbers; or just crying. Lack of this innate system of specialized brain circuitry blights their every attempt to come to grips with even the simplest elements of the national curriculum.

The existence of dyscalculia is a strong argument for an innate basis for mathematical abilities. Since exposure to the normal range of educational experiences, as laid down in the National Numeracy Strategy, seems to cause the dyscalculic child only suffering, is there some other kind of experience that could help them achieve normal levels of maths competence in a pain-free way? There has been no research on this, but I am putting my money on techniques that will strengthen the basic ideas of numerosity. That, and teaching them to use calculators. None of the evidence I have described here means that dyscalculics need be bad at algebra, geometry or other types of more abstract mathematics.

Recording the activity of single cells in a monkey's cortex, measuring how long infants look at dolls, and studying images from the brains of adolescents born prematurely may all seem to be activities that are a very long way from the desk of the Secretary of State for Education. For the sake of the 5 per cent of our children who are dyscalculic, let's hope they're not.

Quantum computers and the quest for the Dream Machine

PAUL DAVIES

A quantum computer could, in theory, out-compute the whole universe and become the ultimate virtual reality machine.

Moore's Law sounds like a scientific principle, but it is in fact a commercial prediction first enunciated by Gordon Moore, co-founder of the computer company Intel. It states that the processing power of computers doubles every eighteen months. The first computers used bulky vacuum tubes and needed entire buildings to accommodate them. Then along came the transistor, which in turn gave way to the incredible shrinking microchip. With each technological leap, the processing power of computers has soared and the costs have plummeted, allowing manufacturers to penetrate new markets and hugely expand production.

The inexorable rise of the computer's potency is legendary. But how long can it go on?

By cramming ever more circuitry into a smaller and smaller volume, faster information processing can be achieved. But there is a limit to how small electronic parts can be. On current estimates, in about fifteen years chip components will approach atomic size. What happens then? The problem is not so much the particulate nature of atoms as such. Rather it lies with the weird properties of the atomic realm. Here, the dependable laws of Newtonian physics dissolve into the weird ghostliness of quantum mechanics, dominated by fuzziness and uncertainty.

To see what this means for computing, picture a processing chip as a glorified network of switches linked by wires in such a way as to represent strings of binary numbers: ones and zeros. Whenever a switch is flipped, one bit of information is processed; for example, a 0 becomes a 1. Computers are reliable because a switch is either on or off, there can be no ambiguity. But for decades physicists have known that on an atomic scale, this clear-cut either/or property of physical states is fundamentally compromised.

The trouble stems from Heisenberg's uncertainty principle. Put crudely, it says there is an inescapable vagueness, or indeterminism, in the behaviour of matter on the micro scale. For example, today an atom in a certain state may do such-and-such, tomorrow an identical atom could do something different. According to the uncertainty principle, it's generally impossible to know in advance what will actually happen – only the betting odds of the various alternatives can be given. Nature is reduced to a game of chance.

Quantum uncertainty is a basic part of atomic and molecular physics, and it's one of the oddest products of twentieth-century science. So odd, in fact, that no less a scientist than Albert Einstein flatly refused to believe it. 'God does not play dice with the universe,' he famously retorted. Einstein notwithstanding, it is now an accepted fact that, at the deepest level of reality, the physical world is irreducibly random.

When it comes to atomic-scale information processing, the fact that the behaviour of matter is unreliable poses an obvious problem. The computer is the very epitome of a deterministic system: it takes some information as input, processes it, and delivers a definite output. Repeat the process and you get the same output. A computer that behaved whimsically, giving haphazard answers to identical computations, would be pretty useless. But try to compute at the atomic level and that's just what is likely to happen. So on the face of it, the game will soon be up for Moore's Law.

But a very different outcome was foreshadowed in 1981 by the American physicist Richard Feynman, in a visionary lecture delivered at the Massachusetts Institute of Technology. Feynman speculated that the sin of quantum uncertainty might be turned into a virtue. Suppose, he mused, that instead of treating quantum processes as an unavoidable source of error to classical computation, one instead harnessed them to perform the computations themselves? In other words, why not use quantum mechanics to compute?

It took only a few years for Feynman's idea of a 'quantum computer' to crystallize into a practical project. In a trail-blazing paper published in 1985, David Deutsch of Oxford University set out the basic framework for how such a device might work. Today, scientists around the world are racing to be the first to make it happen.

At the heart of quantum computation lies one of the strangest concepts in science, known as superposition. A simple example concerns the way an electron circles the nucleus of an atom. The rules of quantum

'I think there is a world market for maybe five computers'
Thomas Watson, chairman of IBM, 1943

'Computers in the future may perhaps only weigh 1.5 tons'
Popular Mechanics, 1949

'I have travelled the length and breadth of this country and talked with the best people, and I can assure you that data processing is a fad that won't last out the year'
Editor of business books for Prentice Hall, 1957

'But what is it good for?'
An engineer at the Advanced Computing Systems Division of IBM on the microchip, 1968

mechanics permit the electron to orbit only in certain definite energy levels. An electron may jump abruptly from one level to a higher one if enough energy is provided. Conversely, left alone, an electron will spontaneously drop from a higher level to a lower one, giving off energy in the process. That is how atoms emit light, for example. Because of the uncertainty principle, it is normally impossible to pin down when the transition will occur. But if the energy of the atom is measured the electron is always found to be either in one level or the other, never in between. You cannot catch it changing places.

Now comes the weird bit. Suppose a certain amount of energy is directed at the atom, but not enough to make it jump quickly to an excited state. According to the bizarre rules of quantum mechanics, the atom enters a sort of limbo in which it is somehow in both excited and unexcited states at once. This is the all-important superposition of states. In effect, it is a type of hybrid reality, in which both possibilities – excited and unexcited atom – co-exist. Physicists routinely create quantum superpositions in the laboratory, and some electronic components are even designed to exploit them in order to produce desired electrical effects.

'There is no reason for any individual to have a computer in their home'
Ken Olson, president of Digital Equipment Corporation, 1977

'Computer systems should understand how we work and learn in an implicit fashion'
Bill Gates, November 1996

'A computer lets you make more mistakes faster than any other invention in history, with the possible exceptions of handguns and tequila'
Mitch Ratclife, MacWeek

'Do not be bullied by authoritative pronouncements about what machines will never do. Such statements are based on pride, not fact'
Dr Marvin Minsky, MIT

For seventy years, physicists have argued over what to make of
quantum superpositions. What really happens to an electron or an
atom when it assumes a dual identity? How can an electron be in two
places at once? Though there is still no consensus, a fashionable view
is that a superposition is best thought of as two parallel universes,
overlapping each other in a hybrid existence. In the above example,
there are two alternative worlds, or realities, one with the atomic electron
in the excited state, the other with the electron in the unexcited state.

Some physicists think of the alternative worlds as mere phantom
realities, and suppose that when an observation is made it has the effect
of transforming what is only a potential universe into an actual one.
Because of the uncertainty principle, the observer can't know in advance
which of the alternative worlds will be promoted to concrete existence
by the act of observation, but in every case a single reality is revealed –
never a superposition. Other physicists are convinced that all worlds are
equally real. Since a general quantum state consists of a superposition
of not just two, but an unlimited number of alternative worlds, the latter
interpretation implies an outlandish picture of reality: there isn't just
one universe, but an infinity of different universes, existing in parallel,
and linked through quantum processes.

How does all this relate to computation? The fact that an atom
can be in either an excited or an unexcited state can be used to encode
information: 0 for unexcited, 1 for excited. A quantum leap between
the two states will convert a 1 to a 0 or vice versa. So atomic transitions
can therefore be used as switches or gates for computation.

The true power of a quantum computer comes, however, from
the ability to exploit superpositions in the switching processes. To
get an idea of what is involved, imagine a row of coins, each of which
can be in one of two states: either heads or tails facing up. Coins too could
be used to represent a number, with 0 for heads and 1 for tails. Two coins
can exist in four possible states: heads-heads, heads-tails, tails-heads and
tails-tails, corresponding to the numbers 00, 01, 10 and 11. Similarly
three coins can have eight configurations, four can have sixteen and
so on. Notice how the number of combinations escalates as more coins
are considered.

Now imagine that instead of the coins we have many electrons,
each of which can exist in one of two states. This is close to the truth,
as many subatomic particles when placed in a magnetic field can indeed

adopt only two configurations: parallel or antiparallel to the field. Quantum mechanics allows that the state of the system as a whole can be a superposition of all possible such 'heads/tails' alternatives, a state technically known as 'entangled'. With even a handful of entangled electrons, the number of alternatives making up the superposition is enormous, and each can be used to process information alongside all the others. In effect, the system can compute simultaneously in all the parallel universes, and then combine the results at the end of the calculation. This is massive parallel computation, care of Mother Nature. The upshot is an exponential increase in computational power. A quantum computer with a mere 300 particles, for example, would be able to out-compute the whole universe!

Creating superpositions of many-particle states isn't easy (the particles don't have to be electrons). Such states are notoriously fragile, and tend to be destroyed by the influence of the environment, a process called decoherence. Maintaining a superposition is like trying to balance a pencil on its point. So far physicists have been able to attain fairly long-lived entangled states of three or four particles at a time, but researchers in several countries are hastily devising clever ways to improve on this.

Optimists believe 2002 may go down in history as the year the decisive breakthrough happened. In a stunning feat of nanotechnology, a research group led by Robert Clark of the University of New South Wales succeeded in embedding phosphorus atoms one by one in precise locations in a silicon crystal, and attaching microscopic wires to each site. The plan is to use the orientation of the phosphorus nuclei as the quantum equivalent of heads and tails, feeding in and reading out information via the wires to the electronic states of the atoms.

The race to build a functioning quantum computer is motivated by more than curiosity. If we had such a machine at our disposal, it could perform tasks that no conventional computer could ever accomplish. A famous example concerns the subject of cryptography. A standard method of encryption is based on prime numbers. Multiplying two primes is relatively easy. Most people could quickly work out that, say, $137 \times 291 = 39,867$. But going backwards is much harder. Given 39,867 and asked to find the prime factors, it could take a lot of trial and error before you hit on 137 and 291. Even a computer finds the reverse process hard, and if the two prime numbers have 100 digits, the task is effectively impossible, even for a supercomputer.

In 1995 Peter Shor, now at AT&T Labs in Florham Park, New Jersey, demonstrated that a quantum computer could make short work of the arduous task of factorizing large prime numbers. At this stage governments and military organizations began to take an interest, since it implied that a quantum computer would render many encrypted data insecure. Projects were started at defence labs such as Los Alamos in New Mexico. Since then, many universities around the world have set up quantum computing research centres.

Soon mathematicians began to identify other problems that looked vulnerable to solution by quantum computation. Most of them fall in the category of search algorithms – various forms of finding needles in haystacks. Locating a friend's phone number in a directory is easy, but if what you have is a number and you want to work backwards to find the name, you are in for a long job.

A celebrated challenge of this sort is known as the travelling salesman problem. Suppose a salesman has to visit four cities once and only once, and the company wishes to keep down the travel costs. The problem is to determine the routing that involves minimal mileage. In the case of four cities, A, B, C and D, it wouldn't take long to determine the distance travelled in the various alternative itineraries – ABCD, ACBD, ADCB and so on. But for twenty cities the task becomes formidable, and soars further as additional cities are added.

It is too soon to generalize on how effectively quantum computers will be able to short-circuit these sorts of mega-search problem, but the expectation is that they will lead to a breathtaking increase in speed. At least some problems that would take a conventional supercomputer longer than the age of the universe should be solvable on a quantum computer in next to no time. The practical consequences of this awesome computational power have scarcely been glimpsed.

Some scientists see an altogether deeper significance in the quest for the quantum computer. Ultimately, the laws of the universe are quantum mechanical. The fact that we normally encounter weird quantum effects only at the atomic level has blinded us to the fact that – to paraphrase Einstein – God really does play dice with the universe. The main use of computers is to simulate the real world, whether it is a game of Nintendo, a flight simulator or a calculation of the orbit of a spacecraft. But conventional computers re-create the non-quantum world of daily experience. They are ill suited to dealing with the world of atoms and molecules. So another application of quantum computing would be to model quantum systems more effectively.

But there is more at stake here than practical applications, as first pointed out by David Deutsch. A quantum computer, by its very logical nature, is in principle capable of simulating the entire quantum universe in which it is embedded. It is therefore the ultimate virtual reality machine. In other words, a small part of reality can in some sense capture and embody the whole. The fact that the physical universe is constructed in this way – that wholes and parts are mutually enfolded in mathematical self-consistency – is a far-reaching discovery. By achieving quantum computation, humanity will have lifted a corner of the veil of mystery that shrouds the ultimate nature of reality.

Lab rats: the remote-controlled rodent roadshow

TIM RADFORD

Meet roborat, mobile at the click of a mouse and ready to go anywhere.

There are parts of a rat's cortex that represent the stimulation it might feel from its left and right whiskers. There is also a segment of a rat's brain where it feels the sensation of pleasure or happiness. Sanjiv Talwar of the State University of New York reported in *Nature*, on 2 May 2002, that he and colleagues had implanted stimulating electrodes into all three places in the brains of five rats, and then mounted a tiny backpack microprocessor on each animal. They then trained the rats in a figure-of-eight maze to go right or left according to a radio signal from a remote operator, and when the rats did the right thing, rewarded them not with a titbit but a simple buzz of pure pleasure. Once the rats had learned to respond to a 'left' or a 'right' signal delivered to the cortical representations of their left and right whiskers, they were ready to take to the open road – up a ladder, across a narrow ledge, down some steps, through

Austin,
January
2003.

a hoop and down a ramp, all at the fingertip control of a distant human navigator. The researchers had bypassed the normal voice commands and titbit rewards of the animal trainer and appealed – so to speak – straight to the senses, to convert a rat into a human-controlled robot.

'Our rats were easily guided through pipes and across elevated runways and ledges, and could be instructed to climb, or jump from, any surface that offered sufficient purchase (such as trees). We were also able to guide rats in systematically exploring large piles of concrete rubble, and to direct them through environments they would normally avoid, such as brightly lit, open arenas,' they reported.

They foresaw a future for roborat as an agent in search and rescue, and even landmine detection. 'Combined with electronic sensing and navigation technology, a guided rat can be developed into an effective robot that will possess several natural advantages over current mobile robots.'

A spokesman for the Humane Society of the United States said: 'This demeans what it is to be an animal. The technology essentially de-animalizes animals and turns them into machines.' Dr Talwar said the experiments were conducted within National Institutes of Health guidelines and that the rats' behaviour was based on reward; there was no deprivation of food and water. 'Nevertheless, for some there may still appear to be something creepy about using a guided rat for real-world tasks,' he said. 'This must be acknowledged – after all, it will be easy to extend the same method to any species.'

Robotics

How little we know about the uncertainty principle

PHILIP BALL

Heisenberg's uncertainty principle has made the quantum leap from the lab to popular language. But it doesn't mean quite what everyone thinks it means.

HEISENBERG: Are we doomed to disagree then on what happened between us at Copenhagen?

BOHR: But that is the whole point, Werner. You yourself have shown that uncertainty is a fundamental part of nature – that there is always imprecision in our knowledge of things.

The disturbing thing is not that these lines don't appear anywhere in Michael Frayn's play *Copenhagen* (I made them up), but that if they had, few people would have batted an eyelid. For isn't that what

Heisenberg's uncertainty principle tells us: that uncertainty lies at the heart of everything?

In fact, Heisenberg never said any such thing. Some scientists today lament the snappy name that the German physicist chose for his unquestionably remarkable discovery in quantum mechanics. If he'd called it the Principle of Non-Commutation of Conjugate Operators, artists, writers and philosophers might have been less eager to seize on it as a leitmotif for the state of modern humankind.

One of the implications of Heisenberg's discovery is that in some experiments an attempt to make a measurement irrevocably alters the state of the system being measured. If you look, you change what's there. Some have concluded with delight that science has thus been hoist by its own petard – or, as David Lodge put it in the *Guardian* during 2002, 'the discovery in quantum physics that an event is ultimately inseparable from its observation [undermines] the assumption that science is objective and impersonal.'

At the root of this misconception is a contemporary erosion of the notion of metaphor. (Novelists, of all people, should understand the distinction between metaphor and reality, but here Lodge has lost it.) Frayn pulls off *Copenhagen* because he never strays beyond his metaphor. The haziness and conflicts in the recollections of Niels Bohr and Werner Heisenberg of their famous meeting in Copenhagen in 1941, when Heisenberg was working on the German atomic bomb, provide an ironic echo of the 'uncertainty' Heisenberg found in quantum mechanics. Frayn never suggests that the two are in any way causally connected.

Even so, some scientists are too sensitive to misunderstandings of the uncertainty principle to let Frayn get away lightly. This theory 'is often used rather loosely in popular culture to justify all kinds of relativism about truth and values', says John Cleary of the National University of Ireland. 'Even Frayn may be guilty of making such vague connections,' he charges.

In the popular view, Heisenberg, who formulated his uncertainty principle in 1927, identified an inescapable fuzziness at the subatomic scale of quantum mechanics. The common belief is that in this microscopic world we can never quite bring things into focus. But that's not what the uncertainty principle is all about. It basically stems from the order in which one performs mathematical manipulations in the equations of quantum theory. One consequence of this technicality is that there are certain pairs of properties of a quantum system, called conjugate variables, that can never be simultaneously measured with infinite accuracy. Position and speed (or strictly speaking, momentum) are such a pair. The more accurately we measure the speed of an electron, the less accurately we can know its position, and vice versa. Heisenberg's principle tells us how much combined uncertainty must always remain.

This is the metaphor Tom Stoppard uses in his spy play *Hapgood*, in which a character says, 'An electron… defeats surveillance because when you know what it's doing you can't be certain where it is, and when you know where it is you can't be certain what it's doing.' Well, up to a point, Lord Copper. But you can know both things pretty well. The uncertainty generally remains tiny, and becomes relevant at all only when we're dealing with particles small enough for quantum mechanics to apply. Particle physicists have to worry about these things; to biologists, they are irrelevant. Even more significantly, the uncertainty principle applies only to conjugate pairs of variables. You can determine non-conjugate properties of a particle as accurately as you like.

Mathematician John Casti points out that this 'measurement problem' in Heisenberg's theory has become garbled into a common belief that the attempt at measurement itself causes the uncertainty. 'This interpretation is just plain wrong,' he says. The usual argument goes like this: if you want to look at an object, you've got to shine light at it – to bounce photons off it; for a subatomic particle like an electron, a photon is a hefty thing to hit it with, and the act of looking knocks the electron onto a new course; then we're left uncertain about what it was doing originally, before we looked. But in fact, Heisenberg's principle tells us that it all depends on what we're measuring.

One thing it certainly doesn't mean is that whenever scientists draw diagrams of their experiments, they are now obliged to put themselves in the picture. Far from being some mystical, holistic truth, Oxford chemist Peter Atkins sees the uncertainty principle in a positivistic light. 'I take the view that it is a great clarifier of nature', he says, 'for it instructs us to choose: speak Japanese or speak Swahili, but don't mix them.'

All the same, the uncertainty principle is not without philosophical implications. Where does the uncertainty come from? It simply pops out of Heisenberg's mathematical equations, and to the quantum pioneer Erwin Schrödinger that was as far as one should look – he considered the quantum world too alien to look beneath the maths. But Bohr and

Heisenberg wanted more; and here again, they disagreed. To Heisenberg, uncertainty could not be a fundamental aspect of reality, but must just reflect the limitations of quantum theory in describing it. To Bohr, the very specific and precise kind of uncertainty Heisenberg had uncovered was a part of the way the universe was built. Casti sides with Heisenberg: 'Uncertainty is a result about a mathematical description of the real world, not about the real world itself. The physical world may or may not have that kind of built-in uncertainty. We'll never know, since the kind of measurements we can actually make in the real world have nowhere near the resolution that would be needed to test Heisenberg's principle.'

So on the one hand it may be ignorance of reality; on the other, reality of ignorance. Now there's a metaphor – I can feel a play coming on…

Life in the cosmos…
and under our feet

DUNCAN STEEL

Scientists are using a surprising variety of approaches in their quest for clues as to whether we are indeed 'alone'.

Take a census of astronomy news stories during 2002, and you'll find a large fraction of them mention something to do with extraterrestrial life. But it was not always so. As a peripatetic astronomer, I have tended to spend several weeks each year working at NASA-Ames Research Center in the Silicon Valley region of California. In 1988, a small conference there focused on the search for life elsewhere in the cosmos. Fourteen years ago, this subject was beyond the pale in scientific terms, and so the meeting was held off-campus, at a local hotel. It was simply not feasible for a NASA research institute to host such a meeting.

Those were the days of William Proxmire and his 'Golden Fleece'

awards for federally funded programmes which, in the opinion of
Senator Proxmire and his staff, were fleecing the US taxpayer. From
a public-relations perspective, these were something much to be feared.
In 1978 Proxmire had named NASA for an award for 'proposing to spend
$14–25 billion over the next seven years to try to find intelligent life in
outer space.' A decade later the agency was still recovering.

How things have changed since. The great science of the twenty-first
century has often been reckoned to be biology, and it seems that many
space researchers have taken this to heart. Rather than a physical,
inanimate universe out there, far above our realm, they conceive a
biological cosmos, at least in their imaginations. Nowhere is this truer
than within the US space agency. Critics complain that practically half of
all NASA's research budget is now allocated to projects that at least claim
to have some relevance to the question of extraterrestrial life, although
the connections are sometimes tenuous. (If we find a Jupiter-like planet
orbiting another star, does that really tell us much about whether there
are living things spread throughout the galaxy?)

NASA-Ames, the headquarters of the NASA Astrobiology Institute,
has become the focal point for research connected with life in the universe
as a whole. Researchers are investigating how life began on Earth, and
where it might similarly have started and flourished elsewhere in the
solar system, and indeed in other corners of the cosmos. To them, finding
microbial slime on Mars, or algae on a moon of Saturn, would be a
triumph. The flip side of the coin represents those involved in SETI,
the Search for Extraterrestrial Intelligence. They aspire to finding not
just simple life, but intelligent, technological life able to communicate
with us across interstellar distances, using radio transmissions or some
other means. Millions of federal dollars go into astrobiology research,
compared with much smaller sums for SETI.

But it is the possibility of Little Green Men that largely fascinates
the public, and what SETI lacks in governmental funding it makes up
for, at least in part, from private sources. Billionaire Paul Allen, partner
of Bill Gates in the foundation of Microsoft, is helping to fund a new array
of radio telescopes dedicated to searching for possible communications
arriving from 'out there'. This effort is coordinated by the privately
operated SETI Institute, located close by NASA-Ames in Silicon Valley,
and also by the University of California at Berkeley, fifty miles across
the bay.

Simply scouring radio telescope data in order to winnow out any structured (that is, artificial) pulses – the sign that ET is calling to us from his home – presents a major number-crunching challenge, and this is where the public has displayed evidence of unquenchable fascination. At Berkeley someone had the bright idea of harnessing the myriad personal computers sitting idly most of the time in homes and offices around the world, and so SETI@Home was born. Participants log onto a website, download a set of radio data, and then whenever their computer is not being used for other purposes a screen saver program clicks in and starts scanning the data for evidence of artificial signals, rather than simply radio noise from distant stars and galaxies. No successes yet – you would surely have heard about it, if there had been – but the four million enthusiastic participants signed up by the end of 2002 provide a clear signal of a different sort. Vast numbers are intrigued by the question of extraterrestrial life, and want to be involved in the adventure.

The furore that began in 1996 over the claimed fossil evidence for microbial life in a meteorite from Mars also shows how tremendously interested people are in this subject. President Clinton was even informed of this development before NASA announced it to the world. In the six years since, many scientists have attacked the conclusions of the original team, while others have defended them. Whether or not there were ancient Martian nano-bugs, it's clear that the public want to hear about them.

Various European nations have made astrobiology a newfound focus. In Spain and France national astrobiology research institutes have been founded. In Britain, while there is no central British agency coordinating and funding such work, several distinct 'centres for astrobiology' have sprung up, notably at Cardiff University, where Chandra Wickramasinghe and the late Sir Fred Hoyle pioneered ideas of panspermia (the hypothesis that life is spread throughout the universe). More significantly, the European Space Agency has adopted astrobiology as one of its core themes, implicitly if not explicitly. A particular example is the Rosetta space mission to a comet, which gets its name from the famous stone in the British Museum that made the deciphering of Egyptian language and hieroglyphics possible. The original *raison d'être* for Rosetta centred on deciphering the way in which the solar system was formed – comets being primordial rubble and ice left over from when the planets agglomerated.

There was originally no mention of extraterrestrial life in the Rosetta programme, just research into the physical processes that formed our system of planets, comets and asteroids. But as preparation progressed towards the planned launch, in early 2003, press releases from ESA shifted in emphasis towards matters such as the significance of comets to life on Earth, either through the supply of organic chemicals and water to our ancient planet (initially baked dry of such essentials), or else because of the importance of catastrophic impacts in the evolution of terrestrial life – the dinosaurs' bad luck making mammalian development feasible.

Tuned in to the cosmos: never mind the little green men, even extraterrestrial slime would be a big discovery.

Plus of course there is the contentious issue of whether comets themselves might provide the 'warm little pond' in which Charles Darwin suggested that life might have begun. Astrobiology is in vogue. ESA's proposed Darwin project, with a tentative launch date of 2015, will consist of a flotilla of eight satellites flying in stable formation near Earth. Six of them will carry telescopes to study about a thousand nearby stars, one at a time. By combining the light from those six at one of the other two satellites (the hub module), a giant interferometer will be produced. This is an optical system capable of far higher resolution than any single telescope on the ground or indeed in space.

The goals of Darwin are 'to detect Earth-like planets circling nearby stars and to set constraints on the possibility of the existence of life as we know it on these planets'. Although over a hundred stars with accompanying planets have been identified since the breakthrough in 1995, in the main these planets are massive objects like Jupiter. Indeed, all that is measured are gravitational wobbles in the host stars, these being interpreted as being indicative of large planets in orbit. Although a few show evidence of smaller planets, perhaps near an Earth mass, it's not as if we have pictures of them.

Darwin would remedy this. It should return direct optical evidence of the existence of smaller bodies, similar we hope to the terrestrial planets Mercury, Venus, Earth and Mars. Although that evidence, from an interferometer, is not quite the same thing as a photographic image, it would be indisputable and also give us a good idea of the planets' sizes, rather than just masses. We would then know far more about planetary systems circuiting other stars. More than this, though, Darwin could render data demonstrating the existence of life on such planets beyond argument. It will have a spectrometer operating in the infra-red region of the spectrum, to look for features characteristic of oxygen and methane. Find them both, and you've found life.

These atmospheric constituents – oxygen and methane – provide a marker for biotic activity. Although Uranus and Neptune contain methane, this being what makes them appear blue-green, it is in the context of chemically reducing atmospheres, with no free oxygen present. British scientist James Lovelock, of Gaia Hypothesis fame, has pointed out that the simultaneous existence of oxygen and methane requires that they be produced continuously. If it were not this way, one or the other gas would be quickly exhausted by their chemical reactivity (methane is combustible, obviously). Find them both on some distant planet, and you've found a tell-tale sign of life. It may only be algae or grass, rather than those Little Green Men, but it would certainly justify Darwin, and perhaps alter our viewpoint in a major way.

The problem with such missions is that there is always the possibility that you will prove your own assumptions wrong. Just such a thing happened with NASA's Viking landers on Mars in 1976. These carried three experiments designed to identify life. (Actually, one could say that there was a fourth, the panoramic cameras, but they saw no aliens gambolling over the horizon to come and inspect what had landed in their backyard.) Each experiment tested samples of the Martian soil, treating them with test reactants to see whether specific processes would occur which were thought to be incontrovertible evidence for biotic activity.

As it happens, two of the experiments rendered positive results, while the third was equivocal. One might have expected a triumphant declaration of 'Life Found on Mars!' The null result from the third experiment (a gas chromatograph) plus conservative thinking – contrasting strongly with what happened with the Mars meteorite more recently – have led to the Viking data being all but forgotten by most people, the exceptions being those devotees who are convinced that there has been life on Mars at some stage in its history. They point out that the two positive outcomes have never been fully simulated in a laboratory.

So what has been happening on Mars? ESA's Mars Express mission is due for launch in June 2003 and arrival at Christmas, carrying the British-led Beagle 2 landing module. Although it will have no experiments specifically oriented towards finding life on Mars, Beagle 2 does have the potential to identify signs of life. Atmospheric trace gases, for example, may provide a fingerprint, as might carbonate deposits, or differing isotopic ratios for certain elements between atoms held in organic and inorganic molecules.

But doing sophisticated experiments so far away and in such a hostile environment is fraught with difficulty, and many would argue that we first need to know far more about life here on Earth – an argument almost entirely neglected until the past decade. When the British astronomer Tom Gold, who has worked most of his life at Cornell University in New York state, suggested a decade ago that the Earth has what he termed a 'deep, hot biosphere' of subterranean bugs comprising at least half the planet's biomass, many people thought he was crazy. But it looks like he's right. Life on Earth is mostly *within* the planet, not walking around on its surface. This has obvious repercussions for any hunt for life on Mars, and so the ability of the Beagle 2's 'mole' (one of several experiments on a moveable arm) to bore under and into rocks is laudable.

Take the microbe *Bacillus infernus*. It was first identified in a drilling project probing two miles beneath the surface of Virginia. Its name indicates that it came 'from hell' because it's pretty hot down there. The deepest I have ever been is just over a mile down a mine at Broken Hill in Australia, and at such a level the surrounding rock temperature is about 60°C. Refrigerated air must be pumped down continuously to make it possible for the miners to work there, and indeed there is no known multicellular life able to survive for long at temperatures above about 50°C. But this bacterium loves it. Such bugs are called thermophiles, and this one is by no means the record holder. *Pyrolobus fumarii*, which thrives around hydrothermal vents on ocean floors, can reproduce at 113°C. Take it below 90°C and it stops replicating. Claims have been made for species able to go to higher temperatures still.

Many such microbes live on Earth in extreme environments of temperature, pressure, acidity and so on, and they are generically termed extremophiles. Most are members of a new domain of life that was largely unsuspected until the past few decades. The name archaeons was coined for these (although more recent comparisons of their DNA sequences with other living things have shown that they are not quite the primitive root of life that was once thought), and although many archaeons are extremophiles, this is not a general rule – you have archaeons living within your body, for example. But the fact that they largely *do* exist in extreme environments is one of the reasons why their recognition was so long in coming.

Thermophiles comprise one broad class, but elsewhere in the solar system – in the permafrost of Mars, or under the icy crust of Jupiter's moon Europa, for instance – we have to look for psychrophiles, which are microbes able to withstand extreme cold. It is in quest of these that much work has been done by astrobiologists in both the Arctic and the Antarctic in recent years, as well as in cold deserts such as the Atacama in Chile. Mars is not only cold, it's also very dry, and few places on Earth match those conditions as well as the high Andes and the Antarctic Dry Valleys. Yet everywhere we look, life is found.

Apparently sterile sandstone slabs in the Dry Valleys, for example, contain endoliths: tiny plants eking out a living without ever seeing any rain, just a few drops of dew each year. Below the perpetually frozen lakes in those valleys there is liquid water – the *sine qua non* of all terrestrial life, so far as we know – and on the lake beds there are mats of algae. Little light penetrates the ice, but still the algae get by. Does this tell us anything about the chances of life below ground on Mars, or within frigid Europa?

Until recently we assumed all terrestrial life depended on sunlight as its fundamental energy source, but now we know this isn't true. Tom Gold's deep, hot biosphere consists of rock-eating bugs disconnected from what happens in the solar glare on the planet's surface. Whole colonies of plants and animals proliferate around the oceanic vents, deriving their energy from chemical sources (using hydrogen or sulphur). In volcanic springs various thermophiles (and indeed acidophiles) proliferate, producing characteristic coloured rings at different distances from the rising hot water. Sunlight has nothing to do with it.

One such thermophilic microbe produces the enzymes essential for multiplying the DNA chains in the polymerase chain reaction, the one so central to genetic profiling. This reaction necessitates an elevated temperature at which common plant and animal enzymes would break down. Similarly, new cold-water detergents employ enzymes derived from psychrophiles, and stonewashed jeans are battered not with stones, but with enzymes found in alkaliphiles. Research on extremophiles is not just a quest to know more about life in the cosmos.

In the US, substantial government funding goes to programmes targeting basic questions about whether life in any form may exist beyond Earth, but almost nothing goes into searches for extraterrestrial intelligence. The Proxmire effect may still be dominant – after all, the Golden Fleece award was specific to looking for '*intelligent* life in outer space'. But on a broader front, the proper scientific approach to the challenge of extraterrestrial life is being tackled in an entirely appropriate way. It may well be that ET is trying to phone us, but we have no data on which to base any proper estimate of the likelihood of his existence. If we did find extraterrestrial slime, and it was a distinct origination of life (rather than just terrestrial bacteria transferred to Mars in some meteorite flung off the Earth by an asteroid impact), it would give us something to go on. We might then anticipate that life is common throughout the galaxy, and that on at least a few planets elsewhere it may have evolved so as to produce sentient beings perhaps able to communicate over interstellar distances, like us.

Cynics have long said that the field of xeno- or exo-biology (the study of non-terrestrial life) is the only discipline with nothing to study, and they have a point. 'Astrobiology' is a catch-all, coined perhaps to counter that. And astrobiologists do have something to study: life on Earth. Go to the internet site of the SETI Institute and you will find that its mission is to 'explore, understand and explain the origin, nature and prevalence of life in the universe'. The NASA Astrobiology Institute has similar aims. Obviously these include understanding life on Earth, not just searching for it elsewhere.

Based on a statistic of one (that there is life on Earth) we can say nothing about the likelihood of life on other planets until we comprehend how life began on this one. Once we unravel that puzzle, and understand the peculiar niches in which life resides, we will have a far better idea of whether life on a clement planet is likely, or not. And if life thrives around volcanic vents far below our oceans, where the temperatures and pressures are extreme, why not deep below the cloud tops of Jupiter itself, rather than just on one of its moons?

Non-lethal weapons: lasers, phasers, Tasers, Dazers, and People Zappers

DAVID HAMBLING

The latest developments in directed energy weapons.

The shortcomings of non-lethal weapons were highlighted in October 2002 when the siege of a Moscow theatre ended in disaster. A group of Chechen terrorists were holding several hundred people hostage; Russian special forces pumped a knockout gas based on the opiate Fentanyl into the theatre to overpower them. Gas is indiscriminate at the best of times, and healthy terrorists may be affected less than frail hostages. The dose used was so great that more than a hundred hostages died.

The war against terrorism has given a huge boost to the non-lethal weapons industry. In the US in particular there is a growing awareness that asymmetrical conflict (warfare in which one side has a superiority in conventional arms but faces an opponent who has fewer resources but uses unorthodox methods) is likely to be the rule rather than the exception in future, and that non-lethal weapons will play an important part in such conflicts. Massive spending has equipped the American war machine with the hardware to deal with enemy tanks and planes, but there is little in the arsenal for handling less orthodox opponents. Youths throwing stones present troops with the unenviable choice of doing nothing or replying with lethal force, and an angry mob can stop an armoured column simply by standing in the road. Terrorists hide behind hostages or human shields. New technologies are called on to meet the anticipated challenges.

While there have been some developments in traditional non-lethal weapons such as tear gas and baton rounds, it is directed energy weapons – lasers and high-power microwaves – which offer the most promise. Safety requirements mean that baton rounds have to be fired at a low muzzle velocity, limiting their range and making them inaccurate. Directed energy weapons by contrast can be used with far more discrimination, offering pinpoint accuracy at long range. However, there may be other trade-offs which the military is keen to downplay.

'It's the closest thing we have right now to phasers on stun,' says US Marine Col. George Fenton of the Pulsed Energy Projectile (PEP). Developed by the Joint Non-Lethal Weapons Directorate (JNLWD), the PEP is described as creating a bright flash and almost deafening bang at the target. Its shockwave can pack as much punch as a rubber bullet. The PEP can be used at different power levels, giving options from merely distracting or warning the target up to delivering a disabling blow. Some sources say that the PEP can also be used on high power to kill, and the JNLWD are vague about this dual lethal/non-lethal capability.

The PEP is actually a pulse laser. When it first strikes the target it vaporizes what it hits, creating a ball of high-temperature plasma. By a phenomenon known as 'inverse Brehmsstrahlung' the plasma absorbs the rest of the laser energy, causing it to expand so rapidly that the air literally explodes. Critics doubt that the PEP is as innocuous as it is described. The programme is cloaked in secrecy, with very little information available. In particular, the effects of a ball of hot plasma in contact with human flesh have not been released, but results of some early tests suggest that it would cause burns at the least. Dr Jürgen Altmann of the Bochum

Non-lethal
weapons may
not mean to kill,
but who says
that they are
safe?

Verification Project is an expert on the effects of non-lethal weapons, and
he believes that the PEP could be deadly even at lower energy levels.
A shockwave near the mouth or nose could be powerful enough to cause
lung damage. Dr Altmann argues that detailed independent study is
needed for all non-lethal weapons, a call which has been largely ignored.

Police in the US have used the Taser for some years. It fires two darts
trailing wires at the target; once they hit, the wires conduct a stunning
jolt of electricity through the target. The Taser suffers from having a range
of barely seven metres and the fact that it is a single-shot weapon. HSV
Inc. are working on a much more capable wireless version of the Taser.
An ultraviolet laser ionizes the air, creating a conducting channel for a
range of a kilometre or more. This is used to pass a current through the
target in much the same way as a conventional Taser. The device, which
HSV calls a Tetanizing Beam Weapon, is still in its early stages, but there
are already signs that the military (including the defence establishment in
Britain) has taken an interest and that it will go 'into the black', becoming
a classified programme. This will ensure that potential enemies will not
be able to develop countermeasures, but it also means there will be
no public discussion of how safe or otherwise it might be.

One non-lethal laser weapon which is already banned by international

Weapons research

treaty is the blinding laser. Lasers are particularly hazardous to eyesight because they produce a beam of parallel rays of light. Laser light persists as a tight beam at long distance rather than spreading out, and the eye's focusing mechanism tends to concentrate it on to a very small spot on the retina. Even a very low-powered laser can cause permanent eye damage, and lasers designed to cause blindness have been outlawed. However, lasers which cause only temporary or 'flash' blindness are still legal, and there have been several attempts to exploit this loophole.

Early laser dazzle weapons of the 1990s like the Dazer were large and cumbersome. The Dazer consists of a rifle-like weapon, a ten-kilo electronics package and a separate battery pack. Smaller, more rugged weapons based on solid-state lasers have succeeded it. One example is the Laser Dissuader which looks like a chunky torch and weighs less than two kilos but is capable of effectively dazzling at fifty metres. A new US military version, called HALT, is designed to be slung under an assault rifle, so that soldiers have the option of using a non-lethal dazzling laser without having to put down their tried and trusted rifles. HALT is intended initially for use by military police, so that perimeter patrols are not forced to open fire on intruders. However, if it is successful it is likely to be taken up by Special Forces and others.

The problem with laser dazzle weapons is that the margin between a device that is ineffective and one which causes permanent harm is a narrow one. The US says that its weapons are safe if used as directed, but if used at very short range they could blind. In The UK, the Ministry of Defence refuses to comment on British developments in dazzling weapons. However, as British Aerospace are working on a number of laser devices which protect aircraft by using a laser to blind the sensors of heat-seeking missiles, it is safe to assume that the technology exists. Russia and China are also reported to have laser dazzle systems.

In late 2001 the US Marine Corps unveiled a new concept in crowd control weapons. The truck-mounted device is called Vehicle Mounted Active Denial System (VMADS) and fires a beam of millimetre-wave radiation, similar to microwaves. Quickly dubbed the 'People Zapper' by the media, the beam works like a microwave oven by heating the target. The USMC claim that the beam only penetrates a fraction of an inch into the skin and causes a sensation like touching a hot light bulb, encouraging the victim to retreat. Extensive tests on human subjects produced, at worst, a small blister.

However, there were again concerns about the safety of the device, and although it is still claimed to be harmless, a test programme is under way to establish whether exposure to the beam could be carcinogenic. Again, too little information has been released about VMADS in terms of the power levels, beam diameter or the frequency used for there to be any independent verification of its effects. VMADS is the only known product of the US military's non-lethal radio-frequency (RF) programme. But there are hints of a host of other devices, including some said to interfere directly with brain function. A recent paper delivered at the National Defense Association described work investigating the effects of RF weapons on the blood–brain barrier. This barrier is an arrangement of cells which protects the brain from harmful chemicals in the bloodstream. The paper suggests that a beam of radio waves could make the blood–brain barrier more permeable, making the subject susceptible to chemical agents which they would otherwise be immune to. This would make it possible to expose a crowd to a gas (for example, a calmative agent) which had little effect except on individuals targeted by an invisible beam.

The Russians have been reportedly working on RF weapons for at least fifteen years and are said to be well advanced in this area. It is even possible that such a device was used in the Moscow theatre siege, as the approximate location of many of the terrorists was known. However, it is unlikely that details of the operation will be released; even the identity of the gas was withheld for some days, delaying effective medical treatment. The only thing we can say for sure is that 'non-lethal' weapons can quite easily kill.

2002 was clearly a year of significant progress on non-lethal directed energy weapons, but knowledge of this progress has remained the prerogative of a small number of individuals inside the defence industry. Some have argued that this is so that taxpayers' money can be spent without the need to produce visible results, others that it represents a sinister move towards social control through technology. We will only know what is out there when these weapons are used in practice. The risk is that the demands of the war against terror will override legal and humanitarian objections, leading to the development of ethically dubious weapons whose exact effects – non-lethal or otherwise – are unknown even to those who possess them.

Animal behaviour: what's in a mane?

TIM RADFORD

Why brunettes are hot stuff.

Lionesses like their males dark and handsome. Peyton West and Craig
Packer of the University of Minnesota set up dummies in the Serengeti
National Park in Tanzania and proved that when it comes to flowing
manes, lady lions prefer – and male lions defer to – brunettes above blonds.

The mane is a puzzle: the equivalent of a huge woolly scarf is not, in
theory, the ideal wear for life in tropical Africa. Manes vary in colour from
blond to black and can be up to a foot long. Lions in the Tsavo National
Park in Kenya often had no manes at all. Researchers have theorized that
manes might protect males in battle over lionesses, but the guess has been
that like the peacock's tail, or a stag's antlers, a lion's mane serves as an
advertisement for prowess and a demonstration of genetic fitness.

According to *Science* of 23 August 2002, Peyton West set up pairs
of realistic-looking dummy lions about 200 metres from a group of adult
lions. She paired the dummies with short blond or long blond manes

to see if length mattered. Then she paired the dummies with long blond or long dark manes. Having set up her dummies, she then turned on tape recordings of a hyena at a kill, to get her somnolent subjects interested.

Male lions were intimidated by long manes and dark manes. Given a choice between the two, males approached the short-maned dummy nine out of ten times. On the one occasion when males approached the long-maned dummy, the lions were themselves old, with long dark manes. No male lion ever approached a long-maned dummy directly. When confronted with a choice of light- and dark-maned dummies, the male lions approached the light-maned dummy five times out of five.

Lionesses, on the other hand, showed a preference for the darker-maned dummy, approaching it rather than the blond-maned dummy nine out of ten times. Zoologists have been systematically gathering data on the Serengeti lions for almost twenty-five years; by now, they know their lions. West and Packer looked at the records and found that where females had a choice, they chose the darkest maned male in thirteen out of fourteen cases. Mane length, on the other hand, seemed to make no difference. They also looked at cases of blood samples taken from sedated males. That, too, revealed that dark mane hid a darker attraction.

'Dark colour tends to be found in high-testosterone males,' Peyton West said. 'Therefore it isn't surprising that females would prefer darker manes and males would be intimidated. But there is no correlation between testosterone and mane length. We figure males are sensitive to an opponent's mane length because recently injured males have shorter manes.'

She then turned to the question of what it cost a male to sport a mane at all. She recorded body temperatures with an infra-red camera. Males were hotter than females. This might have had something to do with the fact that males were bigger, so she measured the temperatures of the maneless lions of Tsavo. There was no difference between males and females. So the male paid a price for his come-hither hair-do.

'A male with a dark mane may have to work harder to stay cool, behaviourally or physiologically, and is advertising that toughness, along with his toughness in battle,' she said. 'But we didn't find that longer-maned males were hotter than those with shorter manes. It appears that beyond a certain length, there's no further cost to having a mane.'

Crows and tools

TIM RADFORD

What a bird brain can really achieve.

Betty the New Caledonian crow lives in a laboratory at Oxford University. In 2002, she made history. She fashioned a hook out of a piece of straight wire and used it to fish for a delicacy. 'Primates are considered the most versatile and complex tool users,' Alex Kacelnik and colleagues in the Department of Zoology reported in *Science* on 9 August, 'but observations of New Caledonian crows (*Corvus moneduloides*) raise the possibility that these birds may rival non-human primates in tool-related cognitive capabilities.'

New Caledonian crows in the wild systematically make and use two discrete kinds of probe to poke for grubs. Professor Kacelnik began a series of experiments with two crows to see if they could deduce the physical properties of tools from their shape. He put a little bucket containing bits of pig's heart inside a tube, beyond the reach of a beak, and presented his crows with a choice of a straight piece of wire and a hooked one. On trial five, the male had taken the hooked wire, so Betty spontaneously took the straight wire, bent it into a hook, and reached for the morsel. Professor Kacelnik and his colleagues investigated this unexpected talent more systematically. Trials in which the crow dropped the wire down the tube and could not get it out again were declared invalid. But in nine out of ten valid trials, within about half a minute, Betty the crow had wedged one end of the wire in the sticky tape at the base of the tube, or held it in her feet, and then bent the wire into a crude but effective hook with her beak, and fished out the titbit. No one had taught her to do such a thing, and she had never before seen a piece of wire. She gave the impression that crows like her understood certain principles of physics.

'The question is, what kind of physics is it that they understand? If you see a problem, pick up a straight wire and without instruction bend it to the right shape, and then go and extract food, that means in a sense that the animal is behaving as if it understands the required physical properties of an instrument to act as a hook,' mused Professor Kacelnik afterwards. 'It would be wrong to think there is only one kind of intelligence, and it has to be the one that we happen to possess. Animals have the abilities they need for the circumstances in which they evolved and we suspect that these animals are exceedingly clever – if you want to use the word – for the problems they normally face. But it is an open question whether they are exceptionally clever for other kinds of tasks.'

Betty the crow hooks a place in history at Oxford.

NOTES ON CONTRIBUTORS

Philip Ball is the author of *Bright Earth: The Invention of Colour.*

Brian Butterworth is professor of cognitive neuropsychology at University College, London and the author of *The Mathematical Brain.* He is currently trying to persuade the government to put more resources into specialized teaching for dyscalculic children.

Mark Collins and **Adrian Newton** work at the UNEP World Conservation Monitoring Centre in Cambridge.

Paul Davies is professor of natural philosophy in the Australian Centre for Astrobiology at Macquarie University, Sydney and winner of this year's Michael Faraday Prize from the Royal Society. His latest book is *How to Build a Time Machine.*

Keith Devlin is the executive director of the Center for the Study of Language and Information at Stanford University, California. His latest book is *The Millennium Problems: The Seven Greatest Unsolved Mathematical Puzzles of Our Time.*

Graham Farmelo is director of the Dana Centre Project at the Science Museum, associate professor of physics at Northeastern University, Boston and the editor of *It Must be Beautiful: Great Equations of Modern Science.*

Peter Forbes is the translator of Primo Levi's last book, *The Search For Roots.*

Richard Fortey is currently visiting professor of palaeobiology at Oxford University. He is the author of *Life: An Unauthorised Biography* and *Eyewitness to Evolution.*

Henry Gee is a senior editor of *Nature.*

Jonathan Glancey is architecture and design correspondent of the *Guardian*, and a pilot.

Neil Hall is the malaria genome project leader at the Wellcome Trust Sanger Institute in Cambridge.

David Hambling is a freelance science and technology writer based in London. He writes regularly for the *Guardian*'s science pages.

David Horrobin is head of Laxdale Ltd, based in Stirling, Scotland and author of *The Madness of Adam and Eve: How Schizophrenia Shaped Humanity*.

Arlene Judith Klotzko is a lawyer and bioethicist. She is writer in residence at the Science Museum, advisor on science and society to the MRC Clinical Science Centre, and visiting scholar in bioethics at the Windeyer Institute, University College, London.

Tim Radford is science editor of the *Guardian*.

Jane Rogers is human genome project manager at the Wellcome Trust Sanger Institute.

Duncan Steel is a physicist at the University of Salford. Once he went looking for non-sentient life under rocks and beer bottles in Outback Australia.

Ben Wisner is a disaster expert at Oberlin College, Ohio and is also affiliated with the Benfield Grief Hazards Research Centre at University College, London and at the Development Studies Institute at the London School of Economics.

Lewis Wolpert is professor of biology as applied to medicine at University College, London. He is the author of *Malignant Sadness: The Anatomy of Depression*.